"I Want You! I Want You to Live with Me."

Brenna looked up, her wide green eyes staring into his dark brown ones, and felt a shiver of anticipation. "For how long?"

Marc smiled, his white teeth gleaming against the tan of his skin. "For as long as this crazy attraction lasts."

Brenna tried to swallow, but there was an aching lump in the way. "I don't know you very well," she prevaricated.

His eyes captured hers, his thumb caressing her wrist. "We'll know each other very well before the month is over, Brenna. That I promise you. . . ."

RITA CLAY

has tried almost every job once. This former bookstore manager has also sold cosmetics and worked in a bank, and ran her own modeling school before turning to writing. Her sense of humor is reflected in her books, along with all the love she has known from her husband and four children.

Dear Reader:

I'd like to take this opportunity to thank you for all your support and encouragement of Silhouette Romances.

Many of you write in regularly, telling us what you like best about Silhouette, which authors are your favorites. This is a tremendous help to us as we strive to publish the best contemporary romances possible.

All the romances from Silhouette Books are for you, so enjoy this book and the many stories to come. I hope you'll continue to share your thoughts with us, and invite you to write to us at the address below:

Karen Solem
Editor-in-Chief
Silhouette Books
P.O. Box 769
New York, N.Y. 10019

RITA CLAY
Sweet Eternity

Silhouette Romance
Published by Silhouette Books New York
America's Publisher of Contemporary Romance

Other Silhouette Books by Rita Clay

Wanderer's Dream
Wise Folly

SILHOUETTE BOOKS, a Simon & Schuster Division of
GULF & WESTERN CORPORATION
1230 Avenue of the Americas, New York, N.Y. 10020

Copyright © 1982 by Rita Clay

Distributed by Pocket Books

ISBN: 0-671-57182-6

First Silhouette Books printing October, 1982

10 9 8 7 6 5 4 3 2 1

Map by Ray Lundgren

America's Publisher of Contemporary Romance

Printed in the U.S.A.

This book is dedicated
to all the Gallaghers from Michigan . . .
especially my mother, Rita Gallagher

Chapter One

When Brenna Gallagher got back to work late that afternoon she hastily dropped her purse in the old metal locker and reached for the small sewing kit on the upper shelf. Her uniform had lost another button. That made two this week. And it never failed to happen at the worst time, like right now, when she was in a hurry. Her deft fingers quickly sewed the shiny white button back into place. She cut the thread with her teeth before glancing at her handiwork, then slipped the gray vest over her white short-sleeved blouse. Her matching gray mini-shorts were neat and newly pressed; at least she could be thankful for that. She picked up her matching cap, muttering under her breath as she pushed out the very dented brim. It had never been flattering, but now, with it looking more ragged than ever, she was totally disgusted with it.

"If I had a replacement for that cap, I'd give it to you." Carol, Brenna's roommate and co-worker, stood in the doorway, her slightly chunky body encased in the same uniform, a clipboard in her hand. "But I don't, so you'll just have to look ugly. Maybe it will give the rest of us a chance." She grinned cheekily, wondering how her roommate could be so dissatisfied with her looks.

Brenna was tall and slim with curves in all the right places. She also had the most beautiful rich red-brown hair Carol had ever seen. It flowed over her shoulders in a mass of curls and waves, thick and luxurious—and definitely seductive. That, coupled with small perfect features and sparkling green eyes, made her the envy of most girls.

"I wish I were you, Brenna," Carol sighed. "Then I'd have my degree *and* be able to plan a future with a handsome guy like Lee."

Brenna gave a disgusted harrumph and tossed the offending cap down on the small makeup counter before twisting her hair into a loose knot on top of her head. She shoved a pin into the hastily secured bun before setting the still-dented cap upon it, almost covering her entire head.

"Well," Brenna muttered, sticking stray wisps of hair under the brim, "you're only one semester behind me. Next semester you, too, can drive around the countryside with a sheepskin dangling from your rearview mirror. I'm supposed to be teaching, not chauffeuring a bunch of rich men who shudder at traffic and yell about detour signs."

"School hasn't started yet, Brenna. You'll teach. I'd bet on it," Carol stated complacently. "Besides, with Lee around to hold your hand, what do you want with a career? If I were you, I'd marry him right now and start raising all those little real estate salesmen. Someday he'll be a broker and have his own chain of offices reaching from the Grand Canyon to Tucson."

"You know how conservative Lee is. He wouldn't do anything that wasn't according to plan," Brenna said absently as she adjusted the set of her slim shoulders. "Besides, I didn't spend four years in college to marry and waste it all." She had doubts where Lee was concerned anyway, but there was no sense in thinking about it now. First things first, and right now she had her job to think about.

"Well? How do I look?" Brenna turned to face Carol, giving a snappy salute as she clicked her sandaled heels together.

Carol chuckled. "Like a boy! With your vest buttoned like that no one will know the difference."

"Good. I think I'll leave it like this." Brenna slipped her license from her handbag into her back pocket along with the plastic identification card showing she worked for Brussard Limousine Company. "Okay. What's my first job?"

Carol glanced down at her roster sheet, her eyes widening. "Oh, my gosh! I don't believe it, you lucky duck!" she exclaimed, glancing back to Brenna, then down to the roster sheet again. "You're picking up Marc Lawter and his attorney."

"Who's Marc Lawter?" Brenna asked, confused by the enthusiasm in Carol's voice. She couldn't remember any old movie stars by that name or any other VIP that Carol might be enthused about.

"He's only the top money-winning golf pro this year and destined for even bigger and better things next year, that's who. And he is absolutely gorgeous. I know. I just watched him win a tournament on television last week."

"You watched golf?" Brenna was incredulous. "I've never known you to watch anything but old two-handkerchief movies!"

Carol looked guilty as charged, a small wry smile tugging at her lips. "Remember when I went home to spend the weekend with Dad two weeks ago? Well, he was watching a golf tournament and I sat with him, thinking I was doing him a good turn by keeping him company. Then Marc Lawter came on the screen. That is some man! He just reeks of sex appeal." She grinned broadly. "And do you know who he dates? Cindy Chapman, the actress, that's who!"

Small bells rang in Brenna's head. Now she vaguely remembered seeing him interviewed on television several months back. She had watched, becoming more irritated as the interview continued. He was as good-looking as Carol thought and with just as much sex appeal. But he had come off sounding very macho and extremely chauvinistic. Too much so for

Brenna's taste. But then, most good-looking celebrities were self-centered.

"I'm impressed," Brenna stated dryly, buckling her borrowed sandals tighter so she wouldn't fall out of them. Hers had broken earlier that afternoon and she hadn't had time to get them repaired. "What time am I supposed to pick him up?"

"Good grief! He'll be at the airport in twenty minutes. You'd better hurry!"

Brenna reached for her own clipboard, which held a similar sheet of instructions, then grabbed the keys to car number eight from the large multihooked pegboard against the wall before she virtually ran out the door.

Darn! Why did she always get the rush jobs? The car she had been assigned was a new, luxurious Ford, silver and black. She fleetingly wondered why he had requested a Ford instead of a Cadillac if he was such a celebrity, but all thoughts about her passenger-to-be fled as she concentrated on maneuvering out of the garage and into the Phoenix traffic. She drove down the wide street, passing through the heart of the city. Many of its buildings were in the middle of receiving a face-lift but still kept the original Spanish flavor of the desert town. Brenna turned toward the university before heading for the road that took her to Sky Harbor International Airport. It was midafternoon and in a little while the commuters would be on their way home. She had to take advantage of the relatively empty streets now so she lowered her foot to the floor.

As she reached the entrance to the airport she saw the bright revolving lights of a local police car in her rearview mirror. Her heart hesitated in midbeat before thumping ahead at a stronger pace. She should have known that today was going to be bad. Now she was *really* going to be late.

Brenna smiled prettily at the officer, hoping for leniency, but got only a cheeky grin and a wink as he handed her the speeding ticket. It was a perfectly horrid day! Now she had a moving traffic violation as well as being late in picking up a customer. Wouldn't her godmother be mad! The thought of that anger made Brenna shudder, her already tense nerves tightening even more. Even though Adele Brussard was the owner of the limousine service, as well as her godmother, Brenna knew that she would not be excused for the ticket or her lateness. There was no nepotism at Brussard. If she hadn't hated the thought of being locked in a tall building as a secretary at one of the many electronics firms that made their home in Phoenix, Brenna wouldn't even have bothered with this job. But the job itself was fun, often challenging and constantly different.

Brenna turned into the long palm-lined drive toward the low, sprawling airport. On her right she could see the heat waves rising from the sun-drenched concrete of the runways. It was another scorching day.

She drew up in front of the large canopy-covered entrance, her eyes scanning the waiting people for Marc Lawter, but he didn't seem to be there. She stopped the car and got out, wanting to check with the baggage carriers. She spied a small group of carriers to one side and waved, moving toward them, when a soft, female voice stopped her.

"Pardon me, are you from Brussard?" a tall blonde, obviously wilting in the hot Arizona sun, called to Brenna.

She turned. "Yes, ma'am."

"Good. I'm Mr. Lawter's attorney, Bette Livingston."

She motioned to the waiting baggage boy who stood slightly behind her loaded down with five or six large suitcases and an old, battered vinyl bag containing what were obviously golf clubs. "Mr. Lawter went inside to call your firm. He'll be right out." She sighed heavily, pushing back a strand of limp hair.

The trip had apparently tired her. Now that Brenna was closer to the woman she could see the fine lines of fatigue and age. She was older than she had looked at first but still very attractive.

The baggage boy took Brenna's keys and, after opening the trunk, piled the suitcases one on top of the other in a neat stack with the golf clubs on top. Brenna opened the car door for the other woman, inviting her to sit in the cool back seat. She was either getting ready to cry or was allergic to the dust that the soft breezes carried everywhere.

"Are you all right, Ms. Livingston? Do you want anything?" Brenna asked solicitously.

An image of Marc Lawter calling Mrs. Brussard and complaining that Brenna was keeping a sick woman waiting flashed through her mind, but she dismissed it. First things first. Right now the lady in question needed help.

"Would you like me to get you a cool drink?"

"It's *Miss* Livingston, and I'll be fine as soon as I get some rest. Marc's been on a whirlwind tour of some of his investments in between tournaments and I'm paying for it with my health." She smiled weakly, closing her eyes as she rested her head against the silver upholstery. "I only wish I had his energy. I keep hoping he'll realize he's not made of steel and slow down, but so far I've been out of luck."

"Our weather is probably helping to drag you down. It will take a little time for you to get acclimated," Brenna murmured as she slipped into the driver's seat and turned on the ignition. "I'll get the air conditioning circulating and you'll feel better."

"I hope so. I feel like I walked out of the airport and into a furnace! The hot air singed my lungs, I'm sure. I glanced over at that temperature chart and it only made it worse! It's a hundred and ten and that tells me I've reached the bowels of hell!"

Brenna laughed. "I know. My dad says the same thing and he lives just a little south of us, near Tucson. I love it, though, and you will, too, I'm sure, once you get used to it. We're named after the Phoenix bird in Arabian mythology, you know. It rose from the ashes of its own nest to begin life again."

"This being its nesting place, I presume?" the older woman asked drily. "I believe there's a lot of

14

truth in that particular myth. It's an inferno out there!"

"It's about time the car showed up!" Marc Lawton muttered as the passenger door reopened. The low, husky voice commanded Brenna's startled attention.

Bette chuckled. "If you hadn't been so impatient, Marc, we could have been halfway to the house by now. The car arrived right after you disappeared." As the lawyer spoke she slid across the back seat to allow him to enter.

Brenna felt a blush extend from her neck to her forehead. My goodness! She hadn't been *that* late! She faced forward, refusing to explain to the rude man why she hadn't happened to be here at the exact moment of his arrival. All she had seen of him so far were a pair of dark tan trousers and long slim hands and she had no curiosity about seeing the rest of the body that went with that rude, though admittedly sexy voice. The day had started out rotten, and from the looks of things it wasn't going to get any better.

Her male passenger slipped into the back seat, but before he could slam the door a female voice from outside the car cooed, "Oh, Mr. Lawter, could I have your autograph, please?"

She could almost see the smile in his voice. "Of course. Anything for a lovely lady such as yourself." A definite titter came from the "lovely lady." Brenna could hear the scratch of pen on paper, then the sudden silence. "Can I kiss you on the cheek, too?" the woman asked with a teas. 3 lilt, and Brenna almost snorted with disgust, especially when she heard his answer.

"Of course. What man wouldn't want to be kissed by a lovely lady, especially when she looks like a long-stemmed American Beauty rose?" He was undoubtedly looking at her legs and Brenna was quite sure that the suggestive quality in his voice was a put-on, but the young girl seemed not to realize it as she ducked her head through the door and gave him a resounding smack. She giggled good-bye and then shut the door.

When Marc Lawter spoke a moment later his good humor had disappeared; his voice was low and brooked no argument. "Get going, driver!"

Brenna nodded and cautiously moved away from the curb and into the stream of traffic.

"Do you know where we're going?" he asked imperiously. He sounded as if his day had not been the best either, but at least the women in his life were still keeping him on his plaster pedestal, if that last fan was anything to go by.

Once again Brenna nodded as she glanced down at the clipboard on the passenger seat. Instead of taking them to a hotel she was driving to a house in one of the older and most exclusive parts of the city.

The street was in a neighborhood with one of Phoenix's finest old golf courses and most exclusive country clubs. Leave it to Mr. Smart and Sassy to pick that area, she thought derisively, not bothering to wonder why she should be so riled at a man she didn't know. It must have something to do with her rotten day.

"Honestly, Marc," the female lawyer muttered, and her voice caught Brenna's wandering attention.

"Look at that. I thought those green areas were grass, but they're not! They're painted gravel!" Her voice held incredulity.

Brenna was about to answer when Marc Lawter made the explanation for her.

"Water is too precious to waste on grass in the desert. Besides, Phoenix is known for keeping most of the landscape as desertlike as possible. They're proud of the difference—this city was carved into the desert where no city should have been."

Good explanation, Brenna thought, glad that he had thought to mention the feelings of the residents for their city. They were proud of Phoenix and its differences from other cities. It was uniquely beautiful.

She glanced in the mirror in order to change lanes and encountered dark brown eyes staring questioningly at her. They were set in one of the most classically handsome faces she had ever seen. Brenna's eyes grew wide in surprise and her mouth dropped open. He was even better-looking than he had appeared on T.V. He had heavy-lidded chocolate-brown eyes that blazed with sensuality, jet-black hair with one perfect lock that curled and fell over a broad forehead, a perfect high-bridged nose with slightly flaring nostrils, and a sensuous and fully defined mouth. To top it all off, he even had a small cleft in his square, somewhat stubborn-looking chin. There was no doubt about it. The man was gorgeous!

"Watch where you're going, driver!" he ordered, and Brenna turned the wheel sharply, staying in her own lane when she realized that there was a truck just behind and to her left. She could feel a light blush rising in her cheeks and was thankful she had to keep her eyes on the traffic and her face straight ahead so he couldn't see her expression.

"I'm surrounded by incompetents," he growled in a velvet rough voice. "First, the wrong tickets, my golf clubs misplaced, and now this!" He waved a hand toward her and she could feel her neck muscles tighten. He wasn't the only one who had had a rotten day! And he wasn't her idea of a prize package either, no matter how nice his wrapping!

"Take it easy, Marc." Miss Livingston patted his shoulder, a hint of tired laughter in her voice. "We're in more competent hands than if you were at the wheel. I always get the feeling you want to commit suicide when you're driving."

"That's because you're used to doing forty in a fifty-five-mile-an-hour speed zone, Bette. You're a basic coward," he retorted, but his voice softened considerably. He turned his eyes back to the front, looking at Brenna and once more capturing her attention in the mirror. She would have been aware of those eyes boring into her from across a desert, let alone in the small confines of a car.

"Are you male or female?" he demanded, and Brenna suddenly realized that although she could see all of him, he couldn't see her face at all.

"I'm a driver, Mr. Lawter."

"Good grief, it's a female!" His voice was disgusted, as was the expression on his face, and her ire rose.

18

"Driving over forty, too," she stated dryly, attempting to camouflage her rising temper with a light voice. She was barely able to be civil after the day's events, let alone put up with some arrogant male deciding to show his chauvinism! "I'm sure the company will find someone else to drive you around, if you so desire." Her voice was sugary sweet, but she could cheerfully have pulled over to the side and shoved him out of the car.

"Are the bulk of the drivers women?"

"All the day drivers are female."

"Then one will do as well as another. No woman has any sense when it comes to driving." She had no idea if he thought he was being funny or not, but if he did, then he definitely had a weird sense of humor!

"Perhaps we only do what's expected of us, Mr. Lawter." Once again her voice was sweet and charming. Thank goodness he couldn't see her clenched hands or, even as thick skinned as he probably was, he would notice she wasn't kidding.

"Apparently so, if that ticket on the dash is any indication." There was laughter in his voice, but she wasn't amused. Gorgeous looks did not a personality make, if he was any example! A stinging retort was on her lips, but she clamped her mouth shut in case it decided to burst forth. What was she doing? Her godmother would be furious when she found out how Brenna had behaved with a client! And the way the day was going, this client would probably dispense with the company's services giving *her* as his reason.

19

Brenna drove through downtown Phoenix, her mind preoccupied with the man in the back seat. She was tense, edgy, and wasn't quite sure why. No man should upset her to that point. Even Lee . . .

"Is this what you do for a living? Aren't you trained for anything else?" His voice held a mildly conversational note, but Brenna still saw red.

"I just received my teaching degree, but, unfortunately, school doesn't begin until late August, so I took this job until then. It helps pass the time and pays for the small things in life, like rent and food." Her green eyes shot fire in his direction, but he only chuckled, a sound from low in his throat that did crazy things to her.

She turned onto another street, clenching the wheel even tighter. Thank goodness they were almost at his destination! Two more miles and she could drop him off.

"Wouldn't you know I'd get a spitfire," he murmured, his voice soft so as not to disturb the now sleeping Miss Livingston. "All right, Miss Spitfire. Drive on. I promise to keep my mouth shut as long as you get us to our destination in one piece."

The rest of the trip passed in silence. He had apparently decided to rest. He leaned his head back on the upholstery, his long-lashed eyes closed. Brenna couldn't keep from darting an occasional glance at him as she drove down the wide street.

Tall palms were set in rows along either side of them, shading the car as it passed by. She came to the correct address and slowed down, turning into the drive of a low, rambling one-story stucco home.

The red-tiled roof gleamed in the hot Arizona sun, while the several cacti grouped together in a bed of granite testified to the desert surrounding them.

He must be paying a fortune to rent this place, Brenna thought. But then, he was probably used to the best, if appearance and arrogance were anything to go by.

As the car halted in the driveway Marc straightened immediately, as if he had never slept. Within seconds Miss Livingston was also awake. Brenna shut off the motor and stepped out of the car, shutting the door sharply. She opened the back passenger door for the lady, then walked directly back to the trunk of the car. Mr. Lawter was big enough to get himself out of the car. If she was going to get into trouble, one more thing didn't matter at this point.

The key didn't want to fit into the trunk lock and Brenna tilted her head to the side in irritation. Her hat fell off with the sudden movement and rolled toward the street, stopping short of the curb.

"Blast," she muttered, reaching for it, only to have the single pin holding her hair in its loose bun fall to the drive. Her rich brown hair cascaded past her shoulders in loose waves.

"And to think I couldn't tell if you were male or female!" Marc Lawter murmured. "With those legs and that hair I don't know how I could have mistaken you for anything but female. All female!" he added.

Brenna glanced up at him, turning away quickly when she noticed his intense gaze. She had seen similar looks many times in her college days, but somehow his look was more personal, more devouring, and it made her already tight nerves tingle.

Now that she was able to see him face to face Brenna could see that he was even more attractive than she had originally thought. Creases of experience were etched from nose to mouth, deepening when he smiled. Small crow's-feet splayed out from the corners of his eyes and she wondered if they were from laughter or simply squinting at the sun as he drove the ball along the golf course.

He seemed to be waiting for a response to his earlier observation, so Brenna obliged. "My father will be glad to hear that. He was wondering."

Why did the man have to have such perfect looks and be so totally arrogant?

"To quote an old cliché, Are there more at home like you?"

"Yes, and if you're the proverbial salesman, my father won't even let you on the porch, let alone invite you to spend the night."

"Pity. With more like you he could probably use the diversion of a sane male." Marc grinned engagingly before turning to help his tired companion out of the car.

"Stop teasing her, Marc. Can't you tell she's not the type for your jokes?" The older woman pushed a stray lock of hair away from her tired face. She still looked exhausted; even her expensive suit was in need of a rest.

"She seems to be doing better than average, Bette."

Brenna quickly opened the trunk. "Why don't you go inside, Miss Livingston? I can handle the luggage."

"Very well. I think I will." Bette Livingston reached for the keys Marc held out to her. "I feel like I'm asleep on my feet." She moved slowly across the granite rock garden.

Brenna began pulling the smaller pieces of luggage out of the trunk and setting them on the concrete while, to her surprise, Marc reached for the golf clubs.

"Looks like you could use a new bag. That one is pretty old," Brenna remarked.

"This is just the cover. The clubs and the leather bag inside are in top shape."

"Really? No one would ever know."

"That's the intention. I could almost guarantee that, if they looked too good, too professional, they would get lost between one destination and another. Someone might like to have them just because they belong to a professional."

Brenna hadn't thought of that, but it made sense. Plenty of people she knew would give their eyeteeth to play with clubs that had been used by a professional golfer, if for no other reason than to say that they had tried them.

Marc carried the clubs to the front porch and came back to retrieve more luggage, muttering under his breath.

"I beg your pardon, Mr. Lawter?"

"I said, I wonder why they don't have male chauffeurs. They're a great deal better for this type of work." He grabbed another heavy piece of luggage.

Brenna straightened, hands on hips, her breasts rising and falling with temper. That was the last straw!

"It's so simple I don't know why you didn't deduce it on your own!" She took a deep breath, feeling the restriction of her vest against the full breasts he'd fastened his eyes upon. "Men wouldn't work for this pay!"

Marc Lawter straightened, his eyes narrowing as he watched her anger erupt.

"They only take this kind of work as a second job to supplement their income. So you see, if it wasn't for us 'weak women,' there wouldn't be anyone to drive you around at all!"

"Are you trying to flatter me? Win me over with your charm and grace so I'll use this limousine service again?"

Brenna was infuriated; it was only with the greatest effort that she could speak without shouting. "I'm only trying to explain one of the facts of life to you, Mr. Lawter. We may have equal rights on paper, but this is the way life really is!"

"And what would happen if I complained about your attitude, Miss . . . ?" he asked softly. It was a question she was not about to answer.

She braced herself to look unflinchingly into his heavenly brown eyes. "I would be fired."

She silently hoped he wouldn't notice her knocking knees.

"And then?"

She shrugged. "I'd have to go home to my parents' house until a teaching position opened up." Brenna bent and took the last of the suitcases toward the door. "But I would survive."

"Because you're a woman?"

She stopped, turning slowly to face him. Her chin tilted determinedly while her legs continued to quake. "Because I'm me!"

He chuckled and his mouth quirked delightfully, making him look like a poster for Man of the Year. "Touché!"

They both dropped the luggage at the door. Then, with only a curt good-bye, Brenna walked toward the car, wanting nothing so much as to go home and crawl into a dark corner, hoping the bogeyman wouldn't get her for the foolish way she had acted today.

"Wait, miss," he called imperiously.

She turned, surprised that he would say another word to her. Then her face flooded with embarrassment when she saw why he had detained her.

"I'm paid by the company, Mr. Lawter. I don't receive tips," she said stiffly.

"You mean you never accept them or you just won't take one from me?"

Once more her face turned red, giving her thoughts away.

"I see. I'm to be the complete villain in this little drama, whether I want the role or not. Is that it?"

"I . . . no. I don't mean that. I'm sorry I was rude to you, and knowing how badly I behaved, I can't accept a tip," Brenna said honestly.

He turned his back to her, shrugging his shoulders in dismissal.

"All right, Miss Whoever-you-are. Thank you for a quick brushup on manners. Have a good day."

Then he disappeared into the dark, cool recesses of the house.

Brenna slowly made her way to the car. Why had she behaved that way? What was the matter with her? Her nerves were ridiculously tight, yet she felt as if she had just run a race and won! How confused could she be?

"You've won, all right, Brenna, me girl!" she muttered to herself as she turned the ignition key. "You've just won the right to the unemployment line."

Her father had told her she'd get into trouble with her temper one day. But did it have to be when her job was on the line?

Brenna drove down the street and headed toward the office. By the time she got back Mr. Lawter would have made his phone call to her godmother and she would be out of a job. All Brenna had to do now was think of another reasonable occupation. Maybe she could sell refrigerators in Alaska. . . .

Chapter Two

When she returned to the office early that evening, no one said a word about a Mr. Lawter calling to ask for Brenna's early retirement. She kept waiting for someone to tap her on the shoulder and tell her she was wanted in the inner office. Still, nothing happened. Grabbing her purse, Brenna finished her daily report and filed it. Then she ran out the door.

She would have all evening to wait for the phone call telling her she was dismissed. Perhaps Lee would call, tying up the line long enough so no one from the office could get through. This morning he hadn't known if he would be able to get away from the office, but he had mentioned talking to her later. A small yellow stripe must have grown down her back during the day, labeling her the coward she had never been before. Hiding actually seemed better than a confrontation with Mrs. Brussard.

Suddenly she wanted the reassurance of Lee's voice on the phone, telling her how nice she was, how sweet. Then she remembered his frown as he had lectured her on decorum. He was constantly reminding her to think before doing or saying anything. She was forever promising she would, all the while secretly rebelling against his stuffed-shirt attitude. Ever since they had become engaged two months ago Brenna had realized that something was missing, and as the days grew into weeks she knew that sooner or later she would have to confront the situation and try to resolve things between them. She could feel the stripe down her back again as she told herself that she was just waiting for the right moment.

She reached her apartment within minutes and went directly to the kitchen to fix herself a tall glass of iced tea. The day looked even worse in retrospect. A buttonless uniform, a dented hat, a traffic ticket, and then a run-in with a client. And not just any old client—a Very Important Person. When would she learn? Were the heavens against her or was she against herself? Probably a bit of both, she silently admitted.

The phone rang and she reached for it, hoping it was someone other than Mrs. Brussard. She'd even prefer someone trying to sell her magazine subscriptions.

"If you're not working late, I need you to attend a cocktail party with me tonight. Can you make it?"

Lee's voice was strong, like a beacon in the night, even if his tone was rather chilly.

"I'm free, Lee. What time should I be ready?" Brenna mentally searched her wardrobe for a dress he hadn't seen at least two or three times. There wasn't one.

"About seven o'clock. I'll take you to dinner later."

"I'd like that."

After Lee hung up Brenna stared at the telephone. The conversation had left her feeling more restless than ever. He never spoke the soft words of love she wanted to hear. He was always hesitant to commit himself verbally and Brenna had very mixed emotions about that. Only in the dark confines of the car or in the hallways outside her door was he ever demonstrative enough to satisfy her vanity. Every woman wants to feel desirable to the man she is to marry, but Brenna always felt that her desirability lay only in her beauty, which Lee liked to display so others could appreciate what he owned. It was a disconcerting thought. Was she the bait as he lured clients to buy real estate?

Brenna remembered a few occasions from the beginning of their time together that thrilled her. Back then Lee would take her in his arms as if he held a precious piece of Dresden china, placing small kisses on her face before finally teasing her mouth with his constantly restrained passion. Only then did she feel loved and wanted. . . .

If only he would become a little more assertive, masterful . . . Flashing brown eyes, dark wavy hair, and a tall, lean physique flashed through her mind, but Brenna shook her head to rid herself of the thought.

Foraging through the closet for something to wear was always depressing and tonight was no exception. Brenna finally settled on a sleeveless copper dress with a low V neckline and gathered waist. It set off her tan nicely and Lee had commented once before that he liked it. Brenna set her hair in hot rollers and was just putting on her makeup when Carol walked in. Her roommate stood just inside the bedroom door and watched Brenna tip her lashes with mascara before pulling the rollers out.

"I thought you said Lee had a meeting tonight."

"He does—he decided to bring me along. It's a cocktail party." Brenna brushed the unruly waves into a semblance of order, the coppery tones high-lighted by the sheen of her dress.

"And you're supposed to entertain the men while Lee sells them property," Carol said as she walked to the bed and dropped to the mattress.

"I think he's just lonesome," Brenna said as she coated her lips with gloss. "After all, we are a twosome."

"In that dress you're more likely to become a crowd." Carol nodded toward the low neckline, which hinted at the fullness of Brenna's breasts to perfection. "Every man there is going to love that dress."

"And to think I never gave a second thought to the neckline when Lee complimented me. I thought

he was referring to the color." Brenna giggled.
"Although, bless his heart, he's too nice to say *why*
he liked it."

Carol grunted as she pushed herself back to rest
her head on Brenna's pillow, adjusting it to fit the
curve of her neck. "He'd have to be blind or senile
not to notice, whether he mentioned it or not," she
muttered sleepily.

A moment later she opened her eyes wide to
watch Brenna's reaction to her words. "Have you
looked at the itinerary for tomorrow?"

"No, why? Oh, there's Lee!" she said as the
doorbell rang. Brenna slipped her feet into her small
copper pumps, giving herself one quick look in the
mirror before dismissing the notion that she should
have worn more makeup. "We're going to dinner
after the party, so I'll probably be home late."

"You have a seven o'clock call."

"Don't worry—I'll make it."

They left immediately. Lee, obviously preoccupied, didn't notice Brenna's dress until they were on
their way. She could feel his glance in the darkness
of the car, his eyes traveling to the low neckline. "By
the way, I like your choice. It's one of my favorite
dresses."

"And my only good one."

"Right."

So much for the obligatory compliment, she decided. Lee hadn't said much of anything. He seemed
a thousand miles away, excluding her completely.
Was this how it would be when they were married?

"Where are we going?"

"First, up to a home in the Camelback Mountain area."

The area was nestled on a ridge just outside the city's downtown area and the homes were beautiful, blending with the scenery so as not to detract from the desert atmosphere.

"Then I thought we'd have dinner at that steak house we passed last week," Lee said after a moment.

"Marvelous."

The home was large, plush and expensive, sitting on several acres of desert land with its back patio reaching up the mountainside and into the darkness. The wealthy men and women there were dressed in the height of fashion. Lee looked, as ever, conservative. His lightweight gray suit, white shirt, and blue tie blended in so well that he could have been part of the decor. Brenna sighed. Couldn't he have worn something bright just this once? If there had been just a touch of red in his tie it would have livened up his somber appearance. Brenna shook herself mentally. She had to stop criticizing Lee. It was something that had started just after they had become engaged, and the more they saw each other the more discontented she became. She'd have to find her opening soon; it was obvious that they needed to talk.

The party was boring. The women stood in small groups trading the latest gossip about those who weren't there. Brenna sipped her drink absently, wondering how long it would be before they could gracefully make their exit. Her eyes sought out Lee, standing tall and handsome, his face serious as he listened to his host expound on yet another facet of business. Irritation raced through her body at the prospect of being there much longer, but she quelled it, rising to freshen her drink. Suddenly she heard a now-familiar name and stopped in midstep as she listened with undisguised interest.

". . . and when I phoned to ask him here tonight a woman answered!" the hostess exclaimed, her eyes wide as she made her idea of the woman's function clear by raising her eyebrows. "He finally came to the phone," she continued, "and was charm personified, but we both knew I had interrupted something. His mind was just not on the conversation!"

"Was it that movie star he's been seen with? What's her name? Cindy Chapman?" another woman questioned, her painted eyes as wide as those of her hostess. Brenna could almost see the naughty thoughts traveling through the woman's mind as a sly smile creased her carefully made-up face.

"No, it wasn't her. I saw her in *Tempted* and her voice wasn't the same at all. But I have heard he's thinking of making his winter home here in Phoenix, so I imagine we'll be seeing her before long."

"It was his lawyer," Brenna said, surprising herself with the small contribution.

"I beg your pardon?"

All eyes were trained on her.

"The woman is his lawyer," Brenna repeated

quietly, knowing she shouldn't have opened her mouth at all.

"And how do you know that?" one of the women asked.

"I drive for a limousine service and he was one of my passengers."

"A limousine service? How . . . ah . . . interesting," her hostess murmured, and Brenna decided from the tone that she had just been eliminated from this social group. She had not only admitted that she worked for a living, but she had overshadowed her hostess's knowledge!

"What was he like?" the woman asked, curiosity overcoming her reluctance to mix with the working class.

"Good-looking, rude, and arrogant," Brenna informed them, ignoring the quickening of her heartbeat. Her mind's eye had conjured up a picture of the man as she had first seen him in the rearview mirror. Her eyes had told her he was the best-looking man she had ever seen and nothing since had changed her opinion of his looks, although she knew him for what he was, arrogant and egotistical. He knew he was intensely masculine and recognized the effect he had on women. No man with his attributes could help but know!

"Have you been driving for a living very long?" her hostess wanted to know.

"Just for the summer. When school reopens I hope to teach the primary grades."

"I see," the woman murmured, but Brenna knew

she couldn't understand the necessity of taking a job to pay for food and rent. This woman had probably never worked a day in her life, unless it was to decide which dress best fit her overly plump figure.

"I think it sounds like fun," another woman said rather wistfully. "I worked in a lodge one summer before I was married and I met all kinds of interesting people. It was so invigorating!"

"Are you ready, Brenna?" Lee was at her shoulder and she knew from his tone that he had heard her do the unthinkable. She had mentioned her job. Lee hated to have others know that she did anything as common as drive a car for a living. There was no glamour in her title, nothing for others to "ah" and "oooh" over, so it was best to leave it unmentioned. Brenna bent down and placed her drink on the nearest glass topped table.

"Yes, Lee."

Within minutes they had made their good-byes and were out the door and in the car. Lee hesitated, his hand resting on the ignition switch. "You didn't have to mention your job, you know."

"Is there something wrong with making an honest living?" Brenna felt cold and retreated further into the icy atmosphere rather than be criticized by Lee. "Some people find it admirable."

Lee sighed with exasperation. "You know what some of those people are like, Brenna. Anything that smacks of the plebeian is out." He turned in the small seat, his expression no longer angry. "I need those people until I can get my own clientele going.

35

After that, our plans for the future can be more firmly fixed." He kissed her quickly on the lips, then turned and started the engine. "Until then, even though it's a noble occupation, please don't announce to the world what you do for a living, all right?" he finished briskly, the subject closed.

Brenna leaned back in her seat. She was angry with him, but she knew he wouldn't understand her anger. The thought of pretending to be something she wasn't and never could be went against her innermost feelings. Lee, however, accustomed to taking on the color and atmosphere of his surroundings, would never understand her reasoning.

The restaurant he had chosen was dark and that immediately spelled expensive.

"Are you sure we can afford this, Lee?" she whispered as they were led to their table. "I thought we were on a limited budget."

He gave her a quelling glance as the waiter pulled out her chair. She sat down and accepted the menu but gave him a look that told him that she wouldn't accept silence for an answer.

"We should be able to splurge occasionally, Brenna. Besides, it's good for me to be seen in the better restaurants occasionally. Money begets money."

And snobs beget snobs, Brenna thought, a small sad smile playing about her lips.

"And how is the lady chauffeur this evening?"

Brenna recognized the voice immediately, even before her surprised glance confirmed the identity of the dancing brown eyes and muscular but sleek physique next to her as Marc Lawter. His looks dazzled her, but even stronger was the sex appeal that was only strengthened by the well-tailored and extremely expensive suit he wore. Naturally he wore a tie with just a hint of red in the pattern. He would!

Brenna nodded as if in both acknowledgment and dismissal, but it was too late. Lee was rising, one hand extended in greeting. Brenna could see the cold, calculating look on Lee's face as he sized Marc up as another potential customer to be cultivated.

"How do you do. I'm Lee Heller."

Marc took his hand, his eyes never leaving Brenna's blushing face. "Hello. Marc Lawter."

"The golfer?" Lee asked incredulously, his composure shaken.

"Among other things, yes," Marc answered drily, looking closely at the other man for the first time.

"Brenna, you never told me you knew Mr. Lawter." Lee's tone was openly accusing.

"I drove Mr. Lawter from the airport to his home today, Lee, that's all," she said stiffly, her eyes glued to the menu, but not seeing the bold print. Brenna's every nerve felt the tall, dark man standing less than a foot away from her shoulder.

"I see," Lee said, though Brenna knew he didn't. "Won't you join us for a drink?"

"I'd like that." Marc took a seat, smiling confidently despite Brenna's cold look. "I'm pleased to run into you again, Brenna."

"Really, Mr. Lawter? I thought we'd seen enough of each other this afternoon."

"Oh, no. If I'd known you were going to be my driver I might have rented a house twice as far from the airport just for the pleasure of your company."

Brenna sent a pleading glance at Lee, expecting him to say something. But he just sat there looking confused by the obvious undercurrent in the conversation.

"We might well have come to blows by then, Mr. Lawter." Brenna shifted in her seat, attempting to avoid meeting his eyes, but it was impossible. "And I'm not supposed to hit customers."

"You're not supposed to argue with them, either, but that didn't stop you this afternoon," Marc returned smoothly.

Conversation halted as the waiter took their bar order. Brenna seethed with impotent anger as she listened to Marc give instructions as if he were the host. The nerve of the man, coming to their table as if they were old friends when they had done nothing but insult each other all afternoon! And the nerve of Lee to allow it!

Lee gave a short laugh. "Brenna has an unusual sense of humor, Mr. Lawter. She forgets that not everyone finds the same things funny."

"She and I understand each other very well, Lee," Marc said softly, using the other man's first name as if they were old friends. "Don't we, Brenna?"

"A little too well, Mr. Lawter," Brenna retorted, staring at the small ruby tie clip he wore instead of at his searing, dark eyes. "And you know what they say—'Familiarity breeds contempt.'"

"Brenna!" Lee exclaimed, obviously shocked by this side of her personality.

Brenna had the grace to feel sorry for him. After all, none of this was his fault. She turned to apologize to Marc, only to find him staring deliberately at the neckline of her dress. Brenna resisted the impulse to put her hand up to hide her cleavage from his gaze, knowing he would only be amused by her effort. But she couldn't keep her face from flaming; she knew that he was thinking about how she would look undressed.

A small combo began tuning up in the corner of the large dining area and soon soft music began to waft through the air. Brenna noted the small dance floor and turned to Lee, but her look was intercepted by Marc.

"If your date doesn't mind, would you dance with me?" he asked, making it sound more like a command than a request.

Lee nodded his approval before she could refuse, giving her a look that spoke volumes. It said, "Be nice to him. He's a prospective client."

Not even her icy glare quelled Marc's obvious amusement at the situation. Brenna stood and stoically led the way to the dance floor as the seductive melody pierced the air. Marc's hand came around her waist, sending unwanted heat waves through her body. Brenna instinctively recoiled from his touch.

"Be still and relax, Brenna. I lead and you follow," he murmured, taking her hand in his and pulling her closer to his lean form.

"Like 'Me Tarzan, you Jane'? Isn't that a little outdated?"

"Only to the rest of the world. You and I march to the same drummer, the original rhythm set by men thousands of years ago."

"And does your 'lawyer' march to that same drummer?" She smiled sweetly.

"Jealous?"

"No!"

"Good. My lawyer is just that, a lawyer and a friend. But you're a different story." His voice went even lower as he whispered into her ear, "The rhythm of your dancing makes my mind imagine you in other roles."

"You're despicable!" She wished her heartbeat would slow down. It must be the heat.

"Among other things," said Marc with barely suppressed amusement. "And you're a spitfire. A good match, don't you think? Now mind your manners or your boyfriend will be upset with you for not charming me into buying whatever he obviously wants to sell."

"How did you know?" she asked before realizing that he must have been guessing.

His hand tightened on her spine, his breath a warm breeze on her already heated cheeks. She tried to ignore the responses her body made to his touch, but she couldn't. She was starting to feel ill; she was flushed and her limbs were beginning to tremble.

"I've been there before. It's not hard to see he's selling something." Marc seemed bored with the entire idea; contempt laced his low, husky voice.

"Everyone has to make a living, Mr. Lawter. You play golf for a living, I drive people around in rented limousines, and Lee . . ."

"And Lee?" he prompted, his hand moving up to tingle along her neck.

"And Lee is in real estate."

"I see. Always on the lookout for new customers, especially rich ones. I'm surprised you weren't a good little girl and told him about me."

Brenna ignored his remark. "As I said, Mr. Lawter, everyone has to earn a living."

"Even when it means putting his girl friend on the auction block?"

"I'm not for sale!" Brenna's hand came down from his shoulder to stop the movement of his hand as it caressed her back, but he took it and held it, bringing her into closer contact with him.

The music swirled around them, trapping Brenna in an invisible cocoon. Her taut nerves began to relax to the soft music and her head rested beneath his chin. She felt curiously comfortable with a man she hated, but she didn't want to try to dissect her confused feelings. Marc pulled his head away, staring down into her eyes with a look that touched the recesses of her soul. His smile was slow and easy; then he kissed her forehead and Brenna was sure she was branded by the searing touch.

"If I told him you were going home with me he'd allow it," Marc whispered huskily in her ear. "And you know it."

"He would not. No matter what you say, Lee is a fine, upstanding person." She resolutely pushed aside her own doubts about him. "I'm looking forward to our wedding, so watch what you say." She tried to ignore the feel of his muscled thighs pressed against her own as the music moved them slowly across the floor.

"So, you're supposed to marry him? Then it's a good thing I met you. You need someone to excite you, to put the flush on your face, as I do. Lee will never be able to do that."

Brenna tried to jerk out of his arms, but he held her even closer, almost cutting off her breath.

"It will take some doing, but I'll just have to prove to you that you really belong to someone like me," he added conversationally, a hint of laughter in his voice.

"I'd rather die single than be your wife!"

"Who said anything about marriage? And what a waste for you to give up men. Trust me—I can give you what you need."

"I don't believe this conversation!" She stared at his suntanned face, her eyes blurring until she locked in on his mouth as it curved into a smile. She had to use all her restraint to keep from lashing out at him. "What in heaven's name do you think I would need from the likes of you?"

"Love," he said, softly. "Tender, full, heady love. Starting in the early evening and lasting right through until dawn. The kind of love that makes you want more and more." His look devoured her. "And make no mistake, you would want more, Brenna."

She shook her head, trying not to let confusion get the better of her. Her green eyes glistened as she fought anger and something else that had risen up and responded to his words. He was insane. That was it. And she was insane, too. This was Alice's tea party and they had both been plucked out of reality and thrown into fantasy. She didn't understand why her form molded to his at his insistent pressure. She didn't care. She buried her head in his shoulder and they danced to the last strains of the music in silence.

Tomorrow she would wake up and it would all seem like a strange dream, a dream that both frightened and fascinated her at the same time.

Chapter Three

Brenna's alarm clock echoed through the room. She turned it off and groaned. Her head ached and her body felt worn out from all the tossing and turning she had done. She walked to the window and stared outside, unable just yet to move enough to put coffee on.

Last night she had really made a fool of herself, both with Lee and Marc. After their dance she had sat in absolute silence, only muttering a "Yes" or "No" whenever the two men tried to include her in their conversation. Lee had been bending over backward to be solicitous of Marc and it had sickened Brenna so much that after dinner she had pleaded a headache, intent on going home as soon as possible. The entire evening had been miserable.

Brenna turned; she wanted to kick the side of the

bed from pure frustration, but she decided against it, knowing that the least she would get was a sore toe. She walked down the hall past Carol's room and through the stale-smelling living room on her way to make coffee. Carol must have spent another night with a good book. Cigarettes were piled in the ashtray and a much-handled paperback lay face down next to a glass of warm soda. Brenna stopped, twisting her head to read the title. *The Case of the Two-Timing Mistress.*

Mistress. That's what Marc had proposed making her. What nerve! Couldn't he see that she had taken an instant dislike to him? He was too imposing, too aggressive, too . . . male! In spite of her feelings about the man Brenna's pulse quickened, her mind conjuring him up as he had stood on the dance floor last night.

Within half an hour Brenna had bathed, dressed, and gotten ready for work. The coffee was now ready and she poured two cups and carried them into Carol's room. "Wake up, sleepyhead!"

"Go away. You're the one who has morning duty today, not me!" Carol groaned, turning over to burrow under the covers.

"Come on. I'm ready to leave and you're the grocery shopper for this week. If you don't do it this morning I'll be coming home to an empty cupboard."

"Glory be! She thinks of her stomach at this time of the day!" Carol grumbled, sleepily forcing herself to sit up and blindly reaching for the coffee. She sipped it and leaned back, cradling the cup in both hands. "Mmmm, very good. If you weren't already spoken for I'd try to talk you into sticking to the single life. I never could make good coffee."

"I noticed," Brenna said drily as she took a seat on the edge of the bed.

"Did you have a nice time last night? And how was your golf pro yesterday? Was he as dreamy in person as he is on television?" Carol was finally awake.

"Whoa! Wait a minute and I'll answer your questions one at a time." She glanced at her watch. "That is, if you promise not to ask too many. I have to leave in a minute." Then Brenna ticked off the answers to the already asked questions on one well-manicured hand. "Yes, I had a good time, until I left the car to enter the cocktail party. Two, the handsome golfer was in fine health and bad temper. And three, he's as dreamy as you thought and with a swelled head to match!"

Carol sat up straight, completely awake now. "What do you mean a swelled head?"

"He acts as if he's God's gift to women and all of us should be worshiping him!"

Carol cocked her head to the side. "That wasn't the impression he gave on television when they interviewed him. In fact, the announcer seemed to think he should have been crowing more. They even mentioned what a low profile he tries to maintain."

Brenna snorted. "Only to keep his love affairs out of the public eye."

"What kind of love affairs?"

"He's supposed to be dating some movie star and

he has a female lawyer traveling with him." She ignored the twinge of guilt her accusation brought, remembering his denial of last night. "Besides, his very manner is suggestive!" Brenna defended her stand, knowing it sounded weak.

"He has to date someone—why not a movie star? It takes two to make a date, you know," Carol reasoned soundly. "And his having a female lawyer is no different from you having a male one." She glanced cautiously at her roommate. "As for being suggestive . . . How? Did he make a pass?"

"Yes. Maybe I'll tell you about it tonight." Brenna stood and straightened the collar on her plain gray uniform. It was time for work. "By the way, do you know where I'm headed today?"

"Yes."

With no explanation or further comment Carol once again burrowed into the darkness under the covers. She obviously had no intention of passing on any further information before she heard the full story of Brenna's evening.

Brenna shrugged and headed out the door. Carol could just stay irritated as far as she was concerned. Just because she hadn't immediately given out the full details of how much of a fool she'd made of herself . . . ! No one but Marc Lawter would ever know she had come so close to losing her self-control. True, Marc had been obnoxious last evening, but she had been just as bad yesterday afternoon on the drive from the airport. Besides, Lee hadn't been all that charming either. He should have done more to protect her from a wolf like Marc.

Instead he had been willing to allow her to be with him, alone, on the dance floor. Brenna wasn't sure what Lee should have done to protect her, but he should have done something!

"Oh, no! Not again!" Brenna moaned as she stood in the locker room and stared down at her clipboard, dismayed beyond belief at the name written in big bold letters as her first and only assignment of the day. "Why me?"

"What's wrong?" one of the other drivers, another teacher waiting for school to start, questioned in surprise.

"I can't believe I'm being assigned the same passenger I had yesterday."

"I don't see anything wrong with that," the other woman said.

"Believe me, something is." A sudden thought came to mind and she grinned. "Say, you wouldn't mind switching agendas with me, would you?"

"Well, uh . . ."

"Come on," she wheedled. "He's a golf pro and gorgeous and you'd get along with him great."

Her surprise was evident. "Are you talking about Marc Lawter?"

"The very same. So how about it? Do you want to switch?"

She shook her head. "I'm sorry, Brenna, but I heard your godmother when she was making up the roster last night. He specifically asked for you. She'd fire me if I switched—a customer request is tantamount to a demand."

"Darn! Are you sure he asked for me, or did my

godmother just decide I deserved him?" Her frustration was apparent in the bright blaze of her eyes.

The other woman felt sorry for her as she shook her head. "No, he asked for you by name, I'm sure."

Brenna turned and left the room, almost stomping in her anger. Drat him! What did he want from her, anyway? Hadn't she made it plain yesterday that she wanted nothing to do with him? Was he such an egomaniac that he couldn't tell a brush-off when it was delivered to his face? Then a second thought came quickly on the heels of the first. No, Marc Lawter knew a brush-off all right, so this must be his idea of some form of punishment. Perhaps he thought he could humiliate her by making her drive him around today. Never mind, Mr. Lawter, she thought to herself. I'll turn the tables on you by apologizing for yesterday. That will give you something to think about!

Brenna jabbed the doorbell, then berated herself for it. She would be cool, calm, and incapable of being ruffled into an argument.

Bette Livingston answered the door, looking both more rested and more relaxed than yesterday.

"Oh, hi! Come on in. Marc's on the phone, but he shouldn't be long. He has so many irons in the fire that it's hard to sort them all out."

Bette turned and led the way into the large Spanish-style home. The handmade Mexican tile on the floor gleamed a dark, polished red, accenting the white stucco walls. The furniture was heavy and

ornately carved; the decor definitely fit the style of
the house. It was all very well done, but it didn't
seem to fit her image of Marc Lawter's tastes at all.

The older woman motioned her to a chair and
Brenna sat on the edge of it, her face set in what she
hoped was a mask of indifference. She was conscious
of her crisp uniform and her hair, which she had put
up in a French twist; she didn't want a repetition of
yesterday's scene. She glanced down, hoping she
looked more professional than she felt.

She heard Marc's voice raised in impatience. "I
don't care about the other scenes—they're fine! But
no man can rescue a woman from drowning and
expect his after-shave to still be working. That's
stretching the American public's imagination a little
too far!"

Bette took a stack of papers from the coffee table
and crammed them into her briefcase. Her eyes were
alight with mischief.

"They've finally talked Marc into doing a series of
commercials for an after-shave company, but he
doesn't like the script, as you can tell."

"I see," Brenna answered stiffly. Now the whole
world would have their fill of him.

"I'm glad to see you're in a better mood today,"
Marc said pleasantly as he stepped into the room.
His eyes narrowed at her costume, taking in her high
firm breasts, small waist, and long slender legs
before returning to her neatly done hair.

A shiver ran through Brenna, as if he had also
found something else, something underneath her
skin, hopes and dreams . . . and fears.

Still and all, she had promised herself she would apologize for yesterday's argument, ignoring the scene last night as if it had never happened. He was probably just trying to pay her back in kind for the way she had behaved earlier; it wasn't anything worth taking seriously. Besides, there just weren't that many jobs available for the summer and with college kids hopping on everything that was open she *had* to keep this job.

"Mr. Lawter." She stood and his eyes darted back to her face. "I want to apologize for behaving so badly yesterday. I didn't mean to lose my temper and it was nice of you not to report me. I promise it won't happen again." It sounded as if she had rehearsed it, which she had, but her eyes met his straight on.

He was silent for a moment, returning her stare, then broke into a large, beautiful grin. "I accept, as long as I don't have to apologize for my own behavior last night."

"If you had any sensitivity at all you wouldn't even mention last night," Brenna said, gritting her teeth while just barely maintaining a slender thread of composure.

"You're absolutely right, Miss Gallagher." He smiled again and she felt as if the sunshine were warming her entire body right down to her toes.

Suddenly he was brisk and businesslike. "Now, shall we go? I need an early start to get everything done today."

Bette Livingston had been standing by the door, briefcase in hand, as she watched the scene unfold.

She moved slightly to allow them both to pass, then muttered under her breath, "My, my—how interesting. And getting more so!"

Brenna drove to six different locations in the canyon area. All seemed to be potential sites for a house. His house? At every stop Marc and the lawyer would get out of the car, glance at various papers, and argue over boundaries, view, and location. Brenna stayed in the car, sitting quietly behind the steering wheel. Her opinion wasn't asked and she didn't volunteer, but she did have her favorite location. It was off the beaten path at the end of a dirt road. The site was about four or five acres of partially wooded land dotted with orange and grapefruit trees that had been planted years ago. It was on the edge of a slight bluff that dropped off to allow an outstanding view of the mountains. The morning mist hung low between the peaks, lending the scene an ethereal quality similar to the cover of an old Western novel. It could have been a book of Zane Grey's. After all, his cabin wasn't far from here in the hills dotting the eastern outskirts of Phoenix.

Later they ate at a small roadside restaurant in almost total silence, caught up in their own thoughts.

After lunch they headed out toward the western part of Phoenix to look at sites much larger than those they had seen that morning. Flat land stretched for miles; the dried earth colors were blinding in the sunshine. At least she had proved herself worthy of her salary, Brenna thought. She had found every site without error; she had hardly spoken two words all day, but her professionalism was obvious and that alone made her feel better.

When they finally pulled into Marc's driveway, it was a little after six o'clock in the evening. The summer sun was still high, but Brenna felt ready for bed.

"I'll need you back here around eight o'clock tonight," Marc ordered and she turned surprised green eyes up to him.

"Tonight?" she parroted.

"Of course! This *is* the way you make your living, isn't it?" he asked, giving an impatient sigh. "If you look at your schedule you'll find that I not only hired you for the day, but for the night, too."

All she could do was stare at him. Didn't he realize how much it had taken out of her just to be around him today? Couldn't he see that she was exhausted?

He shook his head, tut-tutting at the thoughts he read as they traveled across her face. His eyes lingered warmly on her full, partially opened lips and she closed them quickly.

"All you need is a nap and you'll do fine." Marc turned to follow his companion to the door, then retraced his steps back to the car, where Brenna sat watching him. "By the way, you did an excellent job today."

He was gone before she could thank him for the compliment, but she glowed all the way back to the office—until she realized that he could have been patronizing her. Suddenly the compliment meant nothing. A feeling of disappointment flooded through her.

She glanced down at the roster, noting that he wanted the Cadillac for tonight, but the Ford again tomorrow morning. How strange.

Brenna arrived just a few minutes early. She wasn't going to give Mr. Lawter any reason to complain. Not after that disastrous first day!

He answered the doorbell immediately, obviously ready and waiting. He stood in the entrance with the light behind him and Brenna was fleetingly reminded of the devil. He was dressed in a white tuxedo, which contrasted sharply with his golden tan and black hair. Her pulse raced even while she silently berated him for being the picture of the perfect male.

"Are you ready, sir?" Brenna tried to ignore the faint smell of soap mixed with the scent of clean, tangy after-shave that wafted to her on the night air. There was no doubt about it. The man should be a movie star.

Bette Livingston appeared directly behind him, her smile bright and her eyes warm as they twinkled merrily at Brenna, as if they knew a secret and would just love to share it. She didn't seem the least bit embarrassed at having the world know of her association with the younger man and it puzzled Brenna. Could it be that, as Marc had said, there *was* nothing to the two of them living under the same roof? They certainly didn't behave like lovers. A small coil unfurled in Brenna's stomach at the unbidden thought of his lovemaking, sending shock waves to the rest of her body.

The party they were attending was being held at the Phoenix Country Club, a posh club that accepted only those who could afford the steep membership. At least two in the car qualified. Brenna would have to sit in the car and read by the glow of the flashlight; she always kept a new historical romance in the pocket of her purse for just such occasions. That, and the thought of being paid time and a half for an evening's work, made the situation livable . . . barely.

As they drove up to the club entrance flashbulbs popped, almost blinding Brenna. So this was what being in the limelight meant!

Marc stepped out of the car, lending a hand to Bette as reporters flocked around asking rapid-fire questions and Brenna watched in amazement as Marc countered their questions with his own, never answering them directly. He was good at verbal fencing. Brenna was reminded of the other evening at the restaurant when he had parried her questions and demands with equal ease.

Later that night, as Brenna snuggled between the sheets, she thought of the day's events. If nothing else had happened, she had seen a completely different side of Marc Lawter than his fans had ever seen—of that she was certain. He was a businessman through and through. He had proved it by working on briefs and contracts all day while they traveled between land sites. He had worked hard and diligently, listening to Bette when there was a difference of opinion, but making up his own mind in the long run. He had been the epitome of a hard-working executive, not a fun-loving playboy golfer.

However, Brenna was certain of one thing: she would never let her guard down with Marc Lawter. The man was just too dangerous to her peace of mind.

Chapter Four

The locker room was empty and she finally had a moment to herself. Brenna held her brother's latest letter in her hand, chuckling over his description of her youngest sister's attempt at horseback riding.

Heather was six years old and should have been riding two years ago, except that she had broken her leg trying to escape from the pigsty. Since then she had found a thousand different excuses to avoid the lessons, all of them working—until now. Little Heather had finally given it a try and decided that the best method was to guide their old plow horse by pulling on his ear, just to make certain he understood which direction she wanted to go. Not only that, but she swore the ride on the old horse's neck was much smoother than if she sat where she should!

Brenna chuckled again. Her brother would be a good writer someday, fulfilling his ambition. He would graduate from high school this year, then go on to college like the older Gallagher children. There were eight in all, and so far three had completed college or were enrolled now. The others were still home or in school. Some money was available for each of them, but they all had to help out, either by working on the ranch or attempting to receive scholarships. But it was fun and Brenna missed them terribly. She missed the constant crowd of people she'd always complained about. She missed having someone around to pour her heart out to or to pour their problems out to her. She even missed the total lack of privacy that a household of ten people created, and her brother's letter made her aware of that fact once more.

Bob, one of the traffic managers, stuck his head around the locker room door. His bright eyes glowed brighter when they saw Brenna.

"Boss wants you. Right now." He grinned, showing chipped front teeth. "Seems like she's in a good mood, though," he said, disappearing around the corner.

Brenna stuffed the letter back into her purse. She would have to wait for another time to finish it. She checked her makeup and ran a comb through her hair, ignoring the butterflies in her stomach. What had she done now that her godmother wanted to see her about? She had been given the job as a concession to her mother, a girlhood friend of Mrs. Brussard. But their friendship still didn't overcome the fact that she and her godmother didn't get along; consequently, Brenna stayed away from her as much as possible.

Brenna put on a bright smile and walked down the hallway to the door that had MANAGER printed on it in bold black letters. It could have said DEVIL and no one would have raised an eyebrow.

"Come in," a strong voice called at Brenna's knock.

"Did you want to see me, Mrs. Brussard?" Brenna asked politely, taking a chair.

The desk was clear, with the exception of a legal-sized manila folder. Mrs. Brussard was glancing over the papers it held, her glasses perched on the end of her nose, where they could be whisked away at a moment's notice. She might be a career woman, but she was still vain.

"I see that you received a traffic ticket two days ago, Brenna." Her tone was censuring.

"Yes, ma'am."

"Was this before or after you picked Mr. Lawter up from the airport?"

"Before."

"Thank goodness for that!" the older woman exclaimed, letting out her breath. "At least that's some consolation."

"It's my first ticket, Mrs. Brussard."

"I know. But I'd rather there be *no* tickets, Brenna. It shows a distinct lack of responsibility on your part." She stood and closed the folder. "However, I had a phone call from Mr. Lawter just a few minutes ago that renews my faith in you. He's leaving town for a while, but when he returns he requests that you be his driver. I told him I thought we could arrange it."

"Is there any way someone else could drive for him, Mrs. Brussard?"

The look that flashed across the older woman's face immediately told Brenna that she should have kept quiet.

"Why? Is something wrong? Is there something you're not telling me?" the older woman questioned, her eyes narrowing.

"No. He's just a demanding customer. I'm sure a male driver could do twice as well with Mr. Lawter," Brenna hedged, crossing her fingers. "Maybe you could convince one to take the day shift."

"Has he made a pass at you?" Mrs. Brussard looked through the bottom of her bifocals, taking in the tinge of pink in Brenna's cheeks.

Brenna hesitated. He had made a pass, but not during working hours. Suddenly she was reluctant to discuss him. Besides, yesterday he had all but ignored her. "No."

"That's enough for today, Brenna," the older woman stated coldly. "You will check the roster for the rest of this week, but remember, you will drive for Mr. Lawter all next week."

Brenna stood, walking stiffly to the door. Her anger was still simmering.

"By the way, Brenna, did Mr. Lawter give you a clue as to where he's building the new golf course he's designing?"

"Golf course?" Brenna repeated stupidly.

"Yes, he's supposed to be choosing a site for the new championship golf course."

"I didn't know." Brenna shrugged. "He hasn't chosen one as far as I know, Mrs. Brussard."

"Very well. That will be all." The older woman stared out the window, her mind already on something else.

The week was quiet, one day running into the next. By Friday night Brenna was so tired that she could hardly keep her eyes open, yet she lay in bed and saw visions of black hair and a pair of dark, teasing eyes that held a promise of exciting things to come as she was whisked around a dance floor. No! Marc was just another womanizer and that she could do without! Besides, she was going to marry Lee and live boringly ever after. Boring? Why did she think that? Lee wasn't boring. At least, he wasn't until she compared him to Marc. . . .

Brenna turned over on her stomach and hugged the pillow. What Marc was offering was something she didn't want, so why all this worry about something that would never be? She closed her eyes and willed herself to sleep while visions of a dark-haired golfer danced in her head. He was holding her close, his hands soothing against her back, his low, husky words arousing her beyond belief.

"And now, ladies and gentlemen, the Greater Milwaukee Open has come to its peak with Marc Lawter and Vince Gerald in a sudden-death play-off for first place. If Marc wins this he will be in the million-dollar winner bracket. What a match this has been! Here comes Marc Lawter now, up to the tee. This hole, as we mentioned earlier, is a difficult hundred-ninety-yard par three, with water on the left . . ."

Brenna sat in front of the television, her eyes never leaving Marc. A half-eaten sandwich sat on the plate in her lap, the glass of iced tea on the floor by her feet all but forgotten in her excitement.

Marc looked so good! He was wearing wine-colored slacks with a white cotton knit shirt trimmed in the same burgundy. His whole outfit spelled "expensive." Just by observing him on television Brenna could sense his masculinity, and apparently the fans who were there felt it, too. The announcer had mentioned the fact that there were more women than he had ever seen before in the crowd, no doubt due to Marc Lawter's presence.

He showed intense concentration as he stared down the fairway to the flag on the green; then he took a few practice swings. After aligning himself for the demanding shot, Marc swung, hitting the ball straight off the tee to arc down the fairway and come to a rolling stop on the edge of the green.

Then Marc's opponent approached the tee. Brenna held her breath. The telephone rang and she reached for it without taking her eyes from the screen. As Brenna grabbed for it, the tea spilled, the liquid soaking into the rug as if it were a sponge.

"Darn!" she muttered into the mouthpiece, not knowing if she was angry over spilling the tea or for having the telephone ring at such an inopportune time. "Hello?" Brenna stretched for her napkin, righting the glass before dabbing ineffectually at the mess.

"I've heard better responses to my calls, but I guess brothers aren't always top priority," Tommy laughed. He was older than Brenna and they were very close, even though he lived in Prescott and she in Phoenix.

"Hold on a minute, Tommy. There's a shot on television I want to watch." Brenna fixed her eyes to the set, though only the crowd was visible. Suddenly Marc filled the screen, his face wreathed in a big smile. The scores flashed below, proclaiming him the winner by a stroke. She couldn't help the feeling of pride that flowed through her and, frustrated with herself, she turned off the set. "All right. How are things going, brother of mine?"

"Pretty good. What's on TV that caught your interest? I've never known you to be a rifle range fan."

"It's not a shooting match. I was watching Marc Lawter play golf." Her voice held a hint of humor; she'd never been known as a golf fan, either.

"Golf? Boy, he must have more sex appeal than the law allows to get you interested in the game!"

Brenna laughed, explaining how she had driven him around while he was in town. She left out the incidents that had made his visit personal to her.

"How did you like him?"

"I didn't. But I was curious about his profession. He just won a sudden-death play-off for first place. He's good, even if his arrogance overshadows his looks."

"Does the lady protest too much?" her brother asked teasingly. "Which reminds me, how is Lee? As stuffy as ever?"

"He's fine," Brenna said shortly. "But I'm sure you didn't call to ask about his health. What's up? You usually don't call until the rates change."

"I'm driving down to see Mom and Dad next weekend and I thought you might want to go along," Tommy answered casually—almost too casually.

"Are you going alone or is this *it?*"

Tommy sighed. "This is it. Janie and I are engaged and I want her to meet the family. She might chicken out when she finds out how many in-laws she's getting."

"You mean you haven't told her about the brood?"

"Yes, but I don't think she realizes what she's getting into. After all, she's an only child from a well-behaved city family."

"Are you trying to talk her out of it, Tommy?" Brenna questioned.

"Not really. I just see so many problems ahead for us. She doesn't realize how much help our family gives to each other, monetarily and emotionally. We've discussed it, but . . ."

"She seemed reasonably intelligent to me." Brenna's tone was dry.

"She is!" Tommy was quick to defend her. "I just want her to know the type of lifestyle I'm striving for—and it's the same as Mom and Dad's. I really want a large family. I want her to be able to share those things with me without wondering if she missed something later. Will you come?"

"I'm sorry, Tommy; I can't. I have to drive on Saturday morning. But keep me posted. And don't worry—I'm sure things will go great."

After Brenna hung up, she stared out the window at the shimmering heat waves rising above the pavement, attempting to gather the thoughts she hadn't defined before.

She and Tommy and the rest of the kids had been raised in an atmosphere of love and companionship. In times of trouble or need the Gallagher clan banded together into a small army, helping each other with whatever had to be done. Looking back, she realized that her parents had a rare marriage and, in turn, had taught their children, by example, what to expect from life—and love.

Would she and Lee have that type of relationship? Something inside her head yelled "No!" but she ignored it. She'd deal with soul-searching another time.

Tuesday came faster than Brenna had anticipated. She wished that she had at least one more day to prepare for meeting Marc Lawter again; someone else had apparently had the honor of picking him up at the airport, but her clipboard told her to pick him up at ten thirty. And that was what paid the rent, or who, if orders were anything to go by.

When she rang the doorbell Marc was quick to answer, ushering her in with a smile. White slacks hugged his lean hips, emphasizing his tan. He was shirtless and the dark hair on his chest traveled in a narrowing line down his body to disappear below his belt. Brenna tried not to stare, forcing her eyes to defy his. A shirt dangled from his hand and he shrugged into it as he led her into the kitchen.

"There's coffee on the table and breakfast ready, if you like." He reached for a small stack of mail piled neatly next to his plate, slitting the envelopes with practiced ease as he sat down.

Brenna reached for the silver pot of coffee in the center of the table. Had he set the table and fixed the breakfast himself? She didn't think so, but she couldn't be sure.

"No, I didn't," he said, answering her unspoken question. "I have a housekeeper back home, Mrs. Phillips, and she kindly agreed to come and take care of me while I finish my work here."

"I didn't ask," Brenna said coldly.

"You didn't have to. Your eyes were darting all around the room. All women seem to have an insatiable curiosity as to how a man survives without the 'little woman' in the background."

"If you really want to know, I was wondering where Miss Livingston was. Isn't she feeling well?"

"She's probably feeling fine by now. She left early this morning for home. To rest and recuperate, as she put it." He grinned. "You aren't by chance thinking that she's the 'little woman' in my life without whom I would not be able to do for myself?"

"I imagine you do very well, Mr. Lawter—by your

standards. Some men can't settle down to one relationship. They haven't developed far enough emotionally."

"Or they've developed past the point of needing a surrogate mother." He took a bite of fluffy golden eggs, then cut a large juicy piece of steak.

He noticed her watching him. "Training food. I played nine holes of golf this morning."

Brenna nodded. He wasn't the type to laze in bed half the morning; he was too vital for that.

"Giving in so gracefully, Miss Gallagher? I would have expected you to be a defender of motherhood, home, and apple pie."

Brenna shrugged her shoulders, conceding the victory. It was too petty to argue over. She wasn't going to get into another slanging match with him. Not this time! "I only discuss topics when I know the other person has the ability to look at both sides objectively."

Marc smiled and she sat transfixed. Once more he had her under his spell. Why did the man have to be so outrageously attractive?

"Very good, Brenna. You have a sharp wit to match your beauty. That's rare in a woman." He leaned back, relaxed, as he surveyed her through thick black curly lashes. "Have you talked to your boss this morning?" he asked lazily.

"No, why?"

"I asked her to discuss your duties with you."

Brenna's spine stiffened and he grinned, enjoying her reaction.

"Why do my duties need to be discussed?"

"What do you think?" He baited her, his eyes narrowing on her quickly rising breasts. She looked ready to do battle.

"If you're speaking of that first day, Mr. Lawter, I've already apologized, which is more than you've done for your insults. It was a bad day for me and you were just another small straw on my already laden back." Brenna stood, then wished she hadn't.

His eyes wandered down her slim form, taking in her narrow waist and long, coltish legs before once again returning to her face. He regarded her steadily, his dark unwavering eyes sending her a message as old as the earth itself.

Her breath caught and her voice gave her away as she said, "However, if you wish to terminate the agreement with Brussard, I understand."

"My discussion with your boss had nothing to do with that incident," Marc stated flatly. "It had to do with that ridiculous uniform you're wearing."

Now she *was* confused! "What's the matter with it?"

"I asked her to tell you to wear a dress, or at least slacks. I don't usually enjoy being driven around, but it's the only alternative for now, what with the amount of paperwork I have to do. I don't have to worry about where I'm going and can keep my mind on the task at hand." He leaned forward. "But I chose a car that wouldn't draw attention to itself only to end up with a woman, no less, driving me around with that nonsensically obvious uniform on her back." His voice lowered, softening his remarks. "So I asked her to tell you to wear something feminine. Something not quite so obvious."

"I see," she murmured. It made sense in a round-about way. At least she knew why he hadn't wanted one of the Cadillacs that were so popular with their other customers. "If you like, I'll change tomorrow."

He stood abruptly, draining his cup with a gulp. "You'll change now, Brenna. We can stop by your apartment on the way out of town. It will be better to start the week off as we mean to go on, don't you think?"

"Yes, Mr. Lawter," Brenna answered, her meek tone belying the anger her green eyes darted his way. The nerve of the man! Was he going to pick out what she would wear, too?

"Fine. I'm sure your impeccable taste will deliver something good to look at and cool, too," he teased, his eyes glistening with mirth at her impotent anger. "And from now on you'll call me Marc. It will look strange if I call you Brenna while you're still spouting 'Mr. Lawter.'"

Brenna's face must have given away her jumbled thoughts for Marc, head tilted back, gave forth an honest, deep laugh from deep in his throat. "Come on, Prickly Pear! The day's going to be over before we ever get any work done."

He reached out to pull her toward the door. The total male virility of him wound around her, strangling any breath she might have left in her throat.

His laugh slowly disappeared as their eyes locked in silent communication.

Unconsciously Brenna reached up to rest her hand on the broad expanse of his chest, feeling the steady thudding of his heartbeat. Marc sucked in his breath; his dark eyes grew darker. He reached for her waist, pulling Brenna into his embrace as if in slow motion, and they both stood poised before completing the inevitable. Marc's head lowered slowly, as if he half expected her to pull away, but she couldn't move. Her eyes searched his face; she wondered if he wanted to kiss her as much as she suddenly wanted him to. She wanted his kiss with every fiber of her being and nothing else mattered at that moment except that he hold her close.

Before his mouth touched hers Brenna felt the electricity sparking between them like small lightning bolts. His touch alone already had her reeling with its impact. Her blood sang with the joyous wonder that this could be so sweet, so wonderful . . . and so much more powerful an emotion than she could ever have imagined. . . .

Marc's lips parted hers, his tongue drawing patterns in the softness of her mouth, teasing her almost beyond endurance. She brought her arms upward to wrap them around his neck and let her fingers tangle in the darkness of his hair. Every part of her slim body was pressed against his, making her aware, as never before, of the difference between men and women, and she reveled in it.

His hands slid sensuously down from her waist to

rest lightly on her hips before pressing her against him, a murmur of surprise and delight echoing in his throat. She had never known such a powerful stimulant as this man's hands and mouth, and the fact that she responded almost shamefully didn't even register right now. She was lost in a spinning vortex that drove every thought from her head. Her heart was thudding in unison with his and she silently answered his unspoken demands. All that mattered was that she was in his arms, feeling things she had never felt before.

Her hand spread over his rippling back muscles, feeling the pleasure she was giving him in his silent response.

The telephone rang and Brenna jumped. Marc's low chuckle reverberated in his throat. His eyes, heavy lidded, allowed his thoughts to rest just beyond her reach.

"Your phone's ringing." Her voice quaked as she stated the obvious, hoping to pull herself together before he realized what an impact his kiss had made on her.

Marc bent and softly kissed the tip of her nose. "Now we both know the state of your hearing," he teased, his warm breath caressing her heated cheek. His hand rested on the curve of her neck for a stroking second before reaching for the wall phone.

"I've been expecting my agent to call this morning. It's probably him—no one else would have such bad timing."

Brenna turned and looked out the window toward

the bright desert garden in the back yard. What in heaven's name had made her act so wantonly? She'd never be able to face him again!

Lee's face rose before her, frowning in accusation, and she cringed visibly. Guilt assailed her from all sides, but she held back the swiftly forming tears. Marc would not see her cry. She would treat this as another of life's lessons and forge on. One thing the Gallagher clan had plenty of was pride.

Chapter Five

They drove in silence to Brenna's apartment. She had no idea what he was thinking and was almost afraid to find out. Occasionally he would sigh and she thought he was about to say something, but he never did. By the time they reached her apartment she was wound up like a top.

"Would you like to wait inside?" Her voice sounded timid even to her and his look confirmed it.

"Such a nice invitation. Your mother did a good job teaching you manners after all," he teased, before swinging with lithe grace out of the car. "Yes, I'm coming in." It sounded as if he would have followed her whether she had asked him in or not.

The apartment seemed extra quiet after the noise of the busy morning traffic, and in her haste to cover the silence she switched on the stereo, flooding the room with soft dreamy music that was made more for lovers than entertaining clients. But it was too late to change it now without being obvious.

"I won't be but a moment," she murmured. "There are some cold drinks in the kitchen if you want." She disappeared into the bedroom, shutting the door behind her. He hadn't said anything about that kiss, but she suddenly wished there was a lock on the door. His very presence seemed to touch off a spark of pleasurable danger.

By the time she had finished dressing the tension in her slim body had eased somewhat and she could see that she was making a big fuss over nothing. Marc hadn't said anything, had he? So why should she make such a big deal about one small kiss? Brenna ignored the fact that his kiss could in no way be considered small.

When she walked back into the living room she was greeted by a smile that was so dazzling it bemused her, and all the grand walls she had built against him tumbled to the ground in clouds of dust.

"You look good enough to eat, especially now that you're out of that silly uniform," Marc said appreciatively, his glance moving over her from head to toe and back again. "Just like I thought you would."

"Are you ready to go?" she asked in her crisp business voice, praying he wouldn't know that she was still quivering inside from his intense look.

"Yes, as soon as I do one thing." He was so close to her now that she wanted to take a step back, but his hands curved around her waist as if they belonged there. She stared up at him, wondering why her body wasn't moving when she told it to. Instead it seemed to have a will of its own, her arms curving around his back as if they belonged there, her lips parting as if remembering past pleasure. He smiled triumphantly before claiming her lips, showing her once more the sensual delights he could command.

She tried to remain passive in his arms, but once again her traitorous body overcame her thoughts and she responded as much as her experience would let her.

"My Brenna," he sighed, giving short kisses to her slim neck. "You're more than I bargained for in the nest of the Phoenix." His lips touched her temples in caressing delight. "Much more," he murmured hoarsely, holding her closer to him as he once more claimed her mouth. She seemed to stop breathing, her pores soaking in the male-scented air around her. Suddenly he gripped her waist tighter and then moved her away from him, smiling into her stunned face.

"But we've got things to do before the sun goes down." Taking her hand in his, Marc led her to the door. He shut and locked it behind them, leading her down the stairs and into the bright light of the day.

The day was a magic time. The colors of the desert surrounded them on all sides as they drove southeast of Phoenix. The Superstition Mountains were but a haze in the distance, looking much the way the old Dutchman must have seen them that first time. There were still searchers for the Lost Dutchman mine, but as of yet no one had found it.

Marc was still checking out locations for what Brenna guessed to be the golf course her godmother had mentioned, although he never said so. Brenna tried to treat this as any other job and ignore the potently virile man beside her in the front seat, but she gave in, knowing she didn't really want to forget his presence. He hadn't opened his briefcase and pulled out work as he had in the past, but encouraged her to keep up a running commentary about Arizona.

"Indian culture is very much a part of Arizona's past *and* future," she finished up. "We have just about everything—mountains, deserts, high plains, deep valleys, and access to foreign ground—Mexico isn't very far away."

"To say nothing of the Grand Canyon and the London Bridge," he said, tongue in cheek. "One natural wonder and one highly unlikely landmark."

"Have you seen London Bridge?" She was surprised at his knowledge of one of Arizona's newest landmarks.

"No, but I've heard about it. Have you?"

"Yes, with my brother. It was quite a sight."

"Tell me about it," he demanded, leaning back and turning his head so he could watch her without being distracted by the scenery outside.

In her nervousness she began talking faster than usual. "Well, it's not the first London Bridge, but the second one, built in eighteen thirty-one. It's all stone—granite, I think—and arches beautifully, with varicolored flags snapping in the breeze. It almost looks like a festival in itself. Next to it sits an English village, complete with shops, an English pub, and a restaurant."

"And how did they get it set up in the middle of nowhere?" he questioned lazily. She could see a smile tugging at the corners of his mouth and forced her eyes forward, her heart skipping a beat as she realized that he must have guessed she was nervous.

"They dismantled it stone by stone and shipped it over to California, then trucked it inland, where it was reassembled. Then the riverbed beneath it was filled. Now there's good fishing and water skiing, along with small boat sailing."

"In the middle of the desert," Marc murmured, and she nodded.

"Did you enjoy visiting your brother?" His sudden change of subject threw her for a moment.

"Of course. Don't you enjoy visiting your relatives?"

"No," he answered harshly, then changed the subject again. "Is that why you're marrying Lee? To start a family of your own?"

"In a sense." She contemplated her answer, stating out loud what she had never before put into words. "I miss my family. I had a very happy childhood and a lot of support from all of them. I guess I'd like to form my own unit of closeness now."

"You're a rarity, then. Most people don't admit to those types of feelings," he said dryly. "But I thought you could only recreate that type of happiness when you marry someone you love."

"That *would* be a prerequisite." She braked as she

made a sharp turn, then stepped on the gas pedal once more, concentrating on that maneuver rather than reacting to this personal conversation. "And what about you? Did you have a happy childhood?"

"No. I'm one of the millions who wouldn't like to repeat the mistakes of his illustrious ancestors." His voice was grim. "And you'd be better off doing the same thing."

She chose to ignore his implication. "But my parents are very happily married! How could I settle for less than they have?"

"By marrying Lee. He's not for you, Brenna. And you know it."

"I also know it's none of your business," she stated primly, closing the discussion. She didn't need to be reminded that things were less than perfect with Lee, but right now his image stood between her and any mistakes she might want to make with the man beside her, and she needed that reminder.

Lee's image popped into her head again and she tried to hold on to it when she realized just how far she had drifted from him in the past week. Drifted? She had been pulled out to sea by a dangerous undertow named Marc Lawter. She stiffened her spine and sat up straight. Marc had just been trying his seduction skills out on her because there were no other available women around, that was all. Don't take it to heart, old girl, she told herself.

His look proved that her actions were a giveaway and she blushed with anger at the thought of being so easily read.

"I think this is the road. The one on the right."

Marc's voice broke into her silent pep talk as he pointed to a spot further up ahead. A large sandy-red cliff stood to one side like a sentry. On the other side of the road was rolling, sandy terrain. "We'll stop here."

Brenna pulled over to the shoulder. The cliff blocked the rays of the sun and it was almost cool here.

"Why here?" she questioned irritably, wondering what this piece of land had to do with a golf course.

Marc climbed out of the car and stretched before taking the keys from her. She watched silently as he opened the trunk and pulled out a blanket and a large wicker basket. Brenna stepped out slowly, watching in unguarded amazement as he motioned for her to follow him to the base of the cliff.

"Talk about Aladdin! Just when did you conjure that up?" She felt irritated, but she wasn't sure why, unless it was because this looked like the perfect seduction scene in a Western movie and it rankled her that he could have been so obvious.

"Mrs. Phillips, my housekeeper, prepared it for me and snuck it into the trunk while you were inside. You shouldn't leave your keys in the car," he chided gently.

"Apparently. You like to keep your secrets, I see."

Marc shrugged, not bothering to look at her as he sighted a spot clear of small cactus and rocks near the base of the cliff. "I knew we'd have a long drive ahead of us and I didn't feel like stopping for a plastic lunch like the one we had the other day. If you don't like my idea, that's your business, but since I'm paying for your time, I decide when to eat, and I would hope that a good employee would follow my lead." He set the basket down, unfolded the blanket, and turned to survey her, his hands on his lean hips. He looked so cool, casual, and elegant. "Do you want to join me or wait in the car?"

"I'll eat. I may not like the idea very much, Mr. Lawter, but I am hungry."

Without responding, he bent over the basket as Brenna began to lower herself onto the blanket. The soft breeze caught a wisp of her hair and she brushed it back as she watched him. When he glanced over at her his smile deepened, unexpectedly twisting her heart, and she turned away to look out over the ragged landscape.

"Don't be mad, Brenna. You know you want to be with me—you've wanted it all morning."

"That's a rotten thing to say. If you had any kindness at all you wouldn't have mentioned that." Her voice was low with emotion and she closed her eyes, afraid to let him see the defeated look there. She *had* wanted him to kiss her. There was no denying it.

"If I had any kindness at all I would have put myself and you out of our misery this morning by taking you into the bedroom and devouring you in one bite." His eyes captured hers as he bent down to her level, his hand reaching for her clenched fist. "We both know that there's a physical pull between us that's very hard to resist. Why don't we bring it out into the open and discuss it? It might help." His voice was warm and rough on her raw nerves.

Brenna shook her head and for the first time in her life no words came to mind. Even her Irish temper had disappeared, leaving her speechless. His hand gave hers a squeeze, his thumb caressing the underside of her wrist. She couldn't be as blunt as he was. It was something she couldn't discuss; she wasn't sure why the attraction was there. She was confused, wandering along a path she had never been on before, and her confusion frightened her as much as his physical demands did.

"Maybe we should stop trying to ignore it and take advantage of the wonders an attraction like this has to offer," he said softly.

She knew he wasn't referring to the scenic splendor spread before them. The connotation was even headier than the fresh wind blowing tangles in her hair before drifting on to touch Marc's body with the same warm breath. She looked up, her wide green eyes staring into his dark brown ones, and felt a shiver of anticipation as she remembered his kisses and the feeling they had evoked. This morning in his kitchen, then at her apartment, she had learned what desire really was, had experienced it fully for the first time in her life. All her other moments with other men became schoolgirl crushes in comparison.

"What are you saying?"

"That I want you. I want you to live with me." He continued to hold her eyes, his thumb still weaving its pattern on her tender skin. "And I think you want the same thing. You may not know it, but your body does."

"For how long?" Brenna's throat was dry. She tried to swallow, but there was a dusty, aching lump in the way.

"For as long as this crazy attraction lasts." He smiled, his white teeth gleaming against the tan of his skin. She wanted to touch the sandpaper texture of his jawline, the curve of his lips, and the arch of his brow. Only the greatest of efforts kept her from reaching out to him.

"I . . . I don't know you very well," she evaded, wondering how she could continue to carry on this absurd conversation. She couldn't go through with this, could she? A little voice in the back of her head warned her to be careful, but she ignored it. There was no harm in talking about an illicit relationship. The harm was in the doing! The little voice inside her laughed, reminding her of her naïveté.

"We'll know each other very well before the month is over, Brenna," he said softly. "That I promise you."

They ate lunch in the shade of the tall cliff, the soft music of Marc's small portable radio accompanying them. Over the good food and a bottle of dry white wine they relaxed and bantered in carefree abandon. Brenna had stretched out next to him. They barely touched except for their held hands. Marc's eyes were closed, his face composed and almost childlike in relaxation. She tried to imagine what he had looked like as a boy; it wasn't hard at all. He would have been a leader; there was that unmistakable stamp on him. She rose up on one elbow and sketched his face with an imaginary finger. What powerful features he had, yet his vulnerability showed through when he relaxed. Her mind reeled with the thoughts that occurred to her. What would it be like to wake up in the morning and have Marc next to her? Would he be a good lover? Her stomach knotted. She knew the answer to that was yes. She shook her head dazedly. Her senses were swimming with her hunger to experience once more his soul-drugging kiss, to feel his lips on hers as he dragged a response from the depths of her, making her act like someone she didn't know.

Two weeks ago she had thought of lovemaking as a natural part of marriage, nothing more, nothing less. Yet since she had picked this man up from the airport she had found herself aware of him, longing for his intimate touch. Was she crazy? He was way out of her league and she had never been more aware of that fact than now. She should have explained earlier that her answer to his proposition had to be no. She should have told him that she thought of men who indulged in such flimsy relationships. What had happened to her famous Gallagher pride?

His hand came up and cupped the back of her neck, surprising her, since his eyes were still closed. He smiled dreamily, his fingers caressing nerve ends she hadn't known she had. Her heart beat a rapid tattoo against her breast.

"Perfect . . . just perfect," he murmured sleepily.

"What is?"

"The way your neck fits the palm of my hand."

"Like a one-size-fits-all glove," Brenna said drily, hoping her wit would act as a barrier against the topsy-turvy sensations that were playing havoc with her stomach.

Marc didn't answer, just smiled again as he pulled her head down. Once more he hesitated just before their lips met, giving her the option of pulling away if she so desired. But she couldn't; she had no will left where he was concerned. She held her breath in wonder. Her reaction was the same as it had been twice before: total acquiescence. She was without a will of her own, wanting to be taken and dominated by this man whose middle name could have been "Magic." She moaned softly as their lips touched, his mouth gently pressuring hers to open like a flower and give him access to the honey inside. He evoked strange sensations that she was loath to stop. It was wrong, but it felt so warm and wonderful! She could breathe the scent of him, after-shave mixed with the clean smell of man, and she loved it.

Before she knew what was happening he had turned her over to lie on her back while he lay above her. His body was cool and heavy, but perfectly right, breaking down any barricades she might still have had. Marc eased himself over her, his hands gently pushing back stray wisps of her hair before he tangled his fingers in the long auburn fullness. He was so tender and gentle and his eyes glowed with loving, so much so that she blushed at his silent message. She hardly noticed as his hand left the tangling tendrils and began to undo the buttons of her blouse. She felt the warm breath of desert air float over her thinly-clothed breasts, teasing her through her sheer nylon bra, and she automatically reached to cover herself. Marc stilled her.

"Don't stop me—I want to see you." His eyes gleamed softly, unable to hide the depth of his feelings, and he undid the front clasp of her bra, freeing her full breasts to receive his gaze.

"No!" She choked out the word, her voice strangled in a vortex of emotions. She wanted him, but she couldn't let him see her. It didn't make any sense. Nothing did.

"Yes. I won't make love to you here, Brenna. I just want to feel you, get to know you. I want you to know me, too, darling." Without waiting for an answer, he bent his head and teased one rosy-tipped breast, forcing her breath from her body as a deep warmth shot through her, flooding her veins to render her muscles immobile. She felt like brandy in winter—hot and cold at the same time.

Her hands stroked his back, feeling the rippling muscles and sinews. She was unable to break the contact with him, unable to let him go. Her hands searched and found the bottom of his cotton shirt, reaching underneath to stroke the warm skin of his chest, feeling the short, wiry hair dance in her palm. His head came up, his gaze focusing on her provocatively parted lips. She moistened them with the tip of her tongue, an unconsciously sensual action. He moaned, covering her lips once more in a kiss that dragged a total response from her, sending a feeling of total lethargy through her to turn bone into water.

"Mmmmmmm, you taste so good, Brenna," he whispered, nibbling on the lobe of her ear. The light stubble on his jaw rasped against her throat, but she loved it and drew him closer. "You could become a habit, like peanuts or potato chips."

She chuckled. He could become habit-forming himself, like breathing.

His voice was low, sounding like she felt: heady with the knowledge of each other's wants and needs. "You want me and I want you—let's go back to the house and make love comfortably and slowly. I want you in my arms. I want to see your lovely body as it flushes a delicious pink with my lovemaking." His mouth trailed kisses toward hers, but when he reached his destination he only nibbled on her bottom lip, teasing her into wanting him. His hands caressed her breasts, working them to a taut, aching fullness. When he finally pulled away she whispered the only words she could. "I can't," she protested, not realizing she hadn't struggled to get away from his grasp even once.

"Why? And don't tell me you don't want me." Marc chuckled softly, his hands tracing erotic patterns over her waist before slipping up to cup one soft breast.

"I don't know whether I do or not."

He pulled himself up, looking down at her, his breathing shallow. "Are you a virgin?" he asked in disbelief.

Brenna nodded, contrarily hoping he would come back and convince her that what they were doing was right. She wanted his warmth, his weight, and without it . . . Her hands began caressing his chest, feeling the layer of hardened muscle beneath the taut skin. She could feel his heart beating irregularly and it gave her a feeling of satisfaction to know that he wasn't as controlled as he sounded.

She opened her eyes and stared into angry brown pools. "You don't have to pretend with me, you know. I don't care whether you're a virgin or not," Marc said coldly. "I'd prefer it if you weren't, as a matter of fact."

His words acted like a shower of cold water, bringing her once more back into the land of reality. "Fine! Now I know your preferences!" Brenna snapped, pulling herself into an upright position and fumbling with her clothes.

She couldn't look at him; she wouldn't allow him to see just how humiliated she was. What had gotten into her? She had never acted this way with a man before, yet today . . .

"I don't like liars, Brenna."

"I don't either." She turned back to face him, her anger overriding everything. Her breasts rose and fell with her breathing. "You're contemptible, do you know that? You try to seduce me when you have your movie star hovering over you and a female lawyer waiting in the wings. And who knows how many other women are waiting to drool over you! You're insatiable! Casanova would really have to work hard to beat your record!"

"Don't get hysterical, Brenna," Marc said coldly. "If you feel guilty, then face it, but don't take it out on others."

"I'm not taking it out on others, just on you!" Brenna's voice rose, more in fear than anger, as she saw all the warning signals flashing in front of her eyes.

"Perhaps you'd like me to treat you like a child and spank you for your 'bad' behavior earlier. Then you could be free of guilt because you'd been punished," he sneered, slipping his shirt back into the waistband of his pants.

He was so composed! And to top it all off Brenna knew that she *was* acting like the child he had accused her of being, but she couldn't seem to help herself.

She turned her back to him, holding herself tightly as if to ward off a chill. Tears welled in her eyes and her breath came in gasps that she tried to contain, but the lump in her throat made it impossible.

Marc's arms encircled her from behind, his chin resting on top of her head. Brenna stiffened, knowing she couldn't throw him off but also knowing she should. If only her body wouldn't continue to betray her every thought by responding to his nearness.

"Look, let's start over. I don't care if you're a virgin or not. It's not one of my particular hang-ups. But I do care that you'd get upset about it."

His hands slid to her waist and he stood back so he could slowly turn her around to face him.

"You might as well face the fact that we're going to have a relationship in the near future. You being a virgin only means that I'll have to wait a little while . . . until you're ready." He shrugged, a small, tender smile playing around his mouth. "I can wait."

"You sound very sure of yourself," she retorted, desperately wishing her equilibrium would return.

Marc's eyes hardened and a muscle along the side of his jaw flared. "I am."

His look held hers for long moments, as if to convince her that he meant what he said. Then he stooped to pick up the basket. "Now help me put this stuff away. I found the piece of property I was looking for, so we can call it quits for today."

Chapter Six

The following morning Brenna picked up the car keys and grabbed at the roster sheet before heading out the door of the office. Her throat was dry, her eyes ached, and there was a decidedly heavy stone lying on her chest. She had fared badly last night, not sleeping until the early hours of the morning. Images of Lee kept creeping into her thoughts. She had done him a great disservice, cheating on him. Even though she hadn't gone to bed with Marc, she felt guilty all the same. She had kissed him and wanted his arms around her, and those feelings should have been reserved for the man she was to marry. Only the thought of tearing down the last remaining stumbling block between her and Marc kept Lee's ring on her finger. If she broke up with

Lee she would be too vulnerable to Marc's suggestions. She was already much too weak to do more than hold on to what little dignity she had left. She needed all her strength and whatever weapons she could muster to keep Marc at bay.

She drove up the street toward the house that Marc rented. Sooner or later she would have to break up with Lee, for she could never marry one man knowing she felt so strongly about another.

Marc was standing in the doorway as she drove up. He looked stunning in white slacks and a maroon and white shirt, mirrored sunglasses hiding his eyes. The expression on his face—what she could see of it—was the duplicate of her own: withdrawn. He slid into the seat beside her, murmured a good morning, and sat back without another word. Silence reigned as they pulled out of the driveway. Glancing at him, Brenna was almost afraid to ask where she was driving today. His lips were grim and a frown brought his dark brows together like a rain cloud on a sunny day.

"Where to?" she questioned quietly, unable to stand the silence echoing in the intimate confines of the car. The bright sun was shut out by the smoked glass windows, and with the aid of the softly blowing air conditioning and the radio sending love songs through the air, they could have been alone together in the privacy of a bedroom.

"Anywhere." There was no emotion in his voice. "Somewhere with people. Show me what Arizona is all about."

Her anger almost erupted. So he didn't want to be alone with her either! She knew she was being contrary, but his words were like a slap in the face.

"Very well, Mr. Lawter." She stressed the name as she swung the car in an arc to travel in the direction they had just left. They were still in the Paradise Valley area of Camelback Mountain. "I'll take you on a tour of the outlying areas. All big towns are more or less alike. Tall buildings, lots of traffic, and some industry, as you already know."

She slowed down to a crawl and pointed to the rock retaining wall they were passing. "This is Barry Goldwater's home. Besides being one of our senators, his ancestors started the Goldwater Department Store."

They could see the long, rambling ranch-style roof now, with several antennas sticking from it like pins. To one side was a large, tall antenna standing by itself. "He's a ham radio operator and has relayed messages from all over the world," she went on stiffly, her anger apparent. "And, of course, he ran for President once." She sped up before he could catch more than a glimpse of the house on the hill. Seconds later she was racing down the next street.

"Very interesting." His tone was dry and she had to force herself not to grin in delight at his discomfort.

"Isn't it though?" she said sweetly. She drove further down another winding street, her foot heavy on the gas pedal. She knew she was behaving recklessly, but a little demon inside kept egging her on. She swung the big car around several tight turns.

Paloverde trees dotted the landscape along with the ever present and prized saguaro cactus, tall and fat with the recent rains. The car chugged up the steep road called Sugar Loaf Hill. "We're approaching the largest mansion in Phoenix, the Walker McCune Mansion, or should I say castle?" She slowed the car at a dead end, circling slowly when they reached the heavily wired barricade. The house stood on the very top of the hill, its soft pink shutters blending with the morning light. It was indeed a castle, modular in design. "It cost over five million dollars to build and the interior has never been completed. It has an ice rink and a bowling alley. The master bedroom"—she waved her hand toward the vast expanse of windows, not really sure which one she was alluding to—"designed for his wife, holds a round bed on an electric turntable so the view can be changed at whim. And her bathtub is filled by a waterfall. A little extravagant, but he thought she was worth it." She turned toward him, finally acknowledging his stare. He had not looked once at the house since the car had stopped.

"As I understand it, Brenna, McCune never even lived in the house. That wife you spoke of left him before it was completed."

"That's true. Perhaps you should look into buying it, Mr. Lawter. It's the perfect place for a seduction —when you're tired of playing one game you can always play another." Her voice was bitter, but she wasn't sure who the bitterness was aimed at, herself or Marc.

"Not a bad idea, but I don't think I want to spend

over five million on games." He sounded bored and his glance flickered over her slim body, then out the window. They were back on the street and heading toward Scottsdale in no time.

Marc's arm was casually draped over the back of the seat, his fingers occasionally touching her shoulder as she turned corners, and she found herself unconsciously edging toward the door.

"Thinking of leaving me in midtown traffic?" She heard the teasing note in his voice and belatedly realized just how childish she was being.

She straightened in her seat. "I just prefer not to be touched." She sounded stilted and knew it.

"That isn't the message I got at the picnic," he murmured drily.

"But that's the message you're getting now."

"All right." He leaned his head back against the seat, looking suddenly tired and defeated, and her heart gave a jump. But she swiftly reminded herself of his actions yesterday and hardened herself against any softening of her emotions.

"And what other delightful points of interest are we driving by at breakneck speed?"

"This time we're going to see something different." A flash of inspiration had hit her and she smiled at the thought of their next stop.

Marc sighed and opened one wary eye. It paid to be cautious with this one. She was constantly full of surprises, as well as beautiful to look at. "Where are we going?"

She hoped he would get into the spirit of the next stop. It had everything she needed to help her keep hold of her senses: something to do, something to watch, and something to eat. And all in a crowd that could have been designed to keep disturbing private thoughts at bay. Besides, he had asked for a tour, hadn't he? Signs announced their destination and Brenna pulled into a large parking lot to join the rows of other cars, as close as she could get to the entrance of what looked like a movie set of an old Western town.

"This is Rawhide, a replica of a small Western town of the eighteen eighties." She opened the car door before he could protest and stepped out, watching him do the same. "I thought you might like to see what Arizona was like before the West was tamed."

"Great."

She looked for some sign of disdain, but he seemed to feel only honest enjoyment at the idea. For a second she was angry. He was supposed to be too sophisticated for this sort of entertainment and in boredom should have followed the pattern she had imagined for him and asked her to drive him home. As if able to read her mind, he grinned at her frustration and extended his hand.

"Can we be friends now? After all, there's not much I can do to you in a crowd of people." His eyes crinkled at the corners, making her feel both foolish and terribly happy at the same time. She slowly placed her hand in his and nodded, an impish smile parting her lips. Once again the barriers were broken and once again she didn't care.

On the outskirts of the small town was a ring of

Conestoga wagons, wooden flatbeds with canvas tightly stretched across their arched framework. The large wooden wheels were almost as tall as she was. Some were the same wagons that had brought people over the hills, mountains, and plains as they wended their way to the golden West. Others had been used on the movie set for *How the West Was Won.*

"The forefathers of the mobile home," Marc remarked, and she laughed, suddenly glad that they were together.

They took their time walking down the dusty street, hand in hand, dodging the burros, chickens, and goats that were running loose. They were all tame and lent an air of authenticity to the town. Brenna could vividly imagine being a young woman of that time coming to town to shop. One goat butted her gently and she was quickly jarred out of her thoughts, while other animals frolicked as if they were in the mountain pastures. Excited children fluttered around them, shouting and pointing to the animals. They gasped in awe at the cowboys sauntering along the wooden sidewalks, guns low on their hips and ten-gallon hats over their almost invisible eyes. They were the extras, the people who put on the gunfight shows.

Then the fight began. Two men called each other out, one walking down the middle of the street, his hand on his gun. He looked to be in deadly earnest as another man came out of the saloon, his hat tipped back and an arrogant smile on his face. Other stunt men were on roofs, behind barrels, and just inside windows, shooting and falling everywhere once the fight began.

After the show was over, they headed for the coolness of the covered sidewalk. Brenna couldn't believe she felt so at ease with the man beside her. He didn't bait or tease her, just looked as if she were the one shining star in his heaven. Knowing that it was only for the hour made it even more poignant and she treasured each moment, storing them away in her memory.

They passed the blacksmith's shop and walked across to the glassblower, who was sitting in the window of his store and demonstrating his craft, turning small bits of molten glass into delicate works of art.

They continued on past the display of carriages and wagons, including the buckboard wagon, sometimes called the pickup truck of the West, a Civil War ambulance, and, Brenna's favorite, a surrey with a fringe on top.

They stepped inside the museum and laughed at some of the memorabilia of the past, such as the old table and settee with arms made of carved buffalo horns that had once been owned by the lady outlaw Belle Starr. There was also a set of gold dishes that Diamond Jim Brady had commissioned especially to honor his guest, Jenny Lind, when she made her first trip to the United States.

"Now that's going a little too far," Brenna giggled.

"Nothing's too good to impress a lady," Marc whispered over her shoulder, his breath warm on her neck. "Especially when the lady is unimpressionable."

They stopped across the street while Marc bought them both large helpings of popcorn from the old-time popcorn vendor's wagon. It was gaily painted and the vendor told them that it had used to work the streets of Denver, Colorado.

"I thought Goldwater's was in Phoenix," Marc said drily as they popped the hot buttered popcorn into their mouths. He motioned with his head toward a sign: GOLDWATER & BROTHERS—THE BEST ALWAYS, hanging above a replica of a store.

"The first chain store to go suburban . . . to Rawhide," Brenna quipped, and he chuckled with her, giving a warm squeeze to her hand and making her feel a part of him.

They took a stagecoach ride that Brenna knew to be a bodyshaker. They bounced over the dusty, almost unseen track that wound out into the desert, flat and dry. The carriage shivered from side to side, throwing Brenna into Marc's arms as they rounded a curve, but she didn't mind at all. A young mother with two small children sat across from them, holding the little girl and tugging at the small boy's pants as he waved out the window at the passing cactus. The boy turned his bright brown eyes toward them for a moment, watching with a wise-owl stare as Marc whispered in Brenna's ear and she chuckled in response.

"Is that your sister?" he questioned with the directness only children can get away with.

Marc's eyes twinkled, but he kept a straight face as he answered. "No, she's not my sister. I'm hoping she's my best friend."

Brenna blushed under his teasing gaze, but she couldn't help the excitement that pulsed through her at the thoughts his words conveyed.

The child assimilated that for a moment, then gave a sage nod. "That's okay then. You can tell your best friend secrets, but sisters never keep 'em."

"Not when they're little," Marc replied solemnly. "But when sisters grow up they keep secrets better than anyone else."

"Really?" The little boy gave a disbelieving glance at his own sister before looking back at Marc. He obviously needed the bigger man's confirmation.

"Really."

The afternoon had passed so quickly that by evening Marc had to remind Brenna just how hungry she should be.

"Would you rather eat here at Rawhide or go to a restaurant in town?" he asked casually as they strolled down the busy main street, now crowded with even more tourists.

"The Golden Belle Restaurant is supposed to have delicious food." Brenna didn't want to disrupt their easy companionship; she would be content to do whatever he wanted and go wherever he led.

The restaurant was a virtual museum. They saw the ornate and beautiful gazebo first, made in Sweden of fine wood and delicate stained glass. Lining the walls of the lobby were nineteenth-century mechanical musical instruments, the forerunners of today's jukeboxes.

They passed the bar and Brenna stuck her head in. It had supposedly been made in France for a saloon in Goldfield. It was said that the teenaged Jack Dempsey used to work at that very bar as a bouncer, and that was where he had first tasted the thrill of boxing.

They sat at a wooden table in a cozy corner and ordered the specialty of the house, steaks cooked over mesquite wood along with beans and baked potatoes and large slices of thick hot toast.

After dinner Brenna and Marc sat back, sipping their coffee and poking at the apple pie with cinnamon ice cream, too full to do it justice. Tension was returning, like an old adversary. Brenna stared into her coffee cup, wondering who would speak first. She could feel his presence as each moment ticked by and the strain was almost unbearable.

Marc spoke first. "The Golden Belle, an apt name." His eyes darkened as he gazed at her. "I think I've found my golden belle. All I have to do now is convince her to jump into my pan."

"From the fire?" She couldn't look up. His eyes told her what she felt already. It was time to erect that invisible wall again if her heart was going to remain in one piece.

"I keep forgetting how shy you are," he murmured. "A redhead with a temper who can take on

100

the world, yet is shy when it comes to being personal."

"We all hide behind something, Marc." She traced the rim of her cup with her finger.

He lifted one arrogant eyebrow. "I am what you see."

A smile dimpled her cheeks as she shook her head slowly from side to side, her chestnut hair swirling around her slender neck. "Oh, no, you aren't. You're as complex as the rest of us—perhaps even more so. You remind me of an iceberg—only a small portion of you is visible to the naked eye. The rest is hidden."

He grinned, making her pulse accelerate, and scraped his chair back so he could stand. Brenna followed suit. He took her arm and led her out the door and into the dusky evening. "Well, my Brenna, we shall see." His breath caressed her neck and she gave an involuntary shudder. Perhaps it was an omen of things to come.

She drove in silence until they pulled into his driveway. Suddenly she wished that the day wasn't over. She waited, holding her breath, for him to say good night and step out of the car, but he didn't move. Finally she turned to him, only to find him looking at her, waiting.

"Now I know how the girl feels when she's taken home by her date." His teasing was infectious and drove the tension away.

"Having now been in both situations, I can honestly say that the man has the best deal. If he doesn't like his date he leaves her at the door quickly; if he enjoys her company he can invite himself in. Either way, he controls the situation."

His voice took on a low, intimate quality in the darkness as he bent his head over hers, taking her chin in his firm fingers, lightly caressing her mouth. "Is that why you're not asking to come in for a nightcap, Brenna? Because you don't like your date?"

She watched his lips form the words, fascinated yet unable to speak.

"Or are you too shy to ask?"

Control yourself, Brenna, that small inner voice warned, and she gathered up her scattered courage, replying huskily, "No, I'm just engaged."

"An engagement that should be broken." A light danced in his dark eyes, as if he could sense her struggle. "Why don't you just admit that you want to come in and we can cut through all the red tape? You know that's where you'll wind up anyway."

That did it! To be coaxed into doing something was one thing, but to have it assumed was another! "But I don't want to have a drink with you and this engagement *isn't* going to be broken." She leaned back out of his grasp, knowing she had put him in his place. She heard the air hiss through his teeth and stared straight ahead, unwilling to see the anger she had caused.

"You wicked little witch. It gave you a lot of pleasure to say that, didn't it?"

The breath she didn't know she was holding left

her lungs in a whoosh. She had expected anger like a blast from a hot furnace. Instead he had sounded amused.

"Yes," she admitted, her eyes mirroring his mirth. He was more dangerous in this mood than in any other.

"Then I expect the customary kiss good night instead." He raised his hand, as if fending off her advances, when in fact she was stunned into inaction. "But just remember, I'm not the type of man who usually kisses on the first date. This is an exception," he admonished her, and after a silent moment they both burst into laughter.

Without realizing how she got there, she was in his arms, her forehead resting against his. Her hand lay against his chest and she could feel the primitive drumbeat of his heart throbbing in unison with her own. He pulled slightly away to gaze down at her, his hands slowly sliding to her waist and pulling her toward him. She could scarcely breathe as she awaited the moment she wanted most in the world. Her lashes fluttered down to hide the desire that flared in her eyes; she was disturbed and confused at the rioting emotions that had tumbled her into this state of acquiescence. Her senses were clamoring for him, his mouth, his hands, while her mind kept telling her it was wrong. She was engaged, and even if she was going to break the engagement she should remain faithful to her fiancé until the deed was done.

"Marc, please." She shook her head as if to shake away the thoughts of what she wanted from him.

"You say that so sweetly that I can't resist." He hadn't understood what she was asking and his open mouth came down over her parted, pleading lips, sending a molten fire rushing through her veins. She was lost in the sensuous caress of his tongue against hers. His hand slipped down to slide against her ribs, then up again to brush the nipple of her breast. The breath was torn from her; stars exploded in her head as his lips left hers to trail down her neck to the contours of her throat, only to find and cling to the soft valley of her cleavage.

"No," she moaned, her mind telling her to retreat, but her body once more betrayed her by forcing itself against the curve of his.

Suddenly he pulled away, his breath sounding as harsh as hers. "All right, Brenna, I'll stop. I don't want you to have any excuses when you finally come to me." And then he was gone, the slam of the car door the only sound.

Brenna stood on the plush grounds that were both Marc's rented back yard and the edge of one of the fairways of the Phoenix Country Club. A golf bag was tossed to the ground, one of the clubs in her hand. Marc bent down and arranged the small white balls in a line in front of her.

She had asked what golf was all about and he had quickly decided to show her the thrill of the game. So far the only thrill had been watching him move with catlike grace as he set up shots and demonstrated his ability to hit the ball. She grinned, wondering what he would think of her description of him. He would probably throw back his head and laugh in that deep, husky way of his.

He glanced up to see her smile and his eyes crinkled with humor, as if he could read her mind. "Now hold the club. This one's called a pitching wedge, with the grip I just showed you, fingers overlapping each other for firmness. That's it." His hands were over hers and she could feel the pressure of his arms around her.

"What's a pitching wedge for, anyway?" she questioned, hoping he wouldn't notice her sudden breathlessness.

"It's probably the most used club in a woman's bag. It's to get you over sand traps and small bodies of water. It takes your ball a short distance with a high loft."

Brenna took a deep breath. The mixture of fresh desert breeze and his tangy after-shave was a heady aphrodisiac, but it was one that she must ignore. She kept her eyes glued to the ground, hoping that he wouldn't notice her sudden nervousness.

"Keep your left arm straight, Brenna. It's not supposed to look like you're at the Queen's tea party," he teased.

She could feel his long length pressed against her back, his muscles rippling as he moved her arms back and forth in an easy swing. His warm breath teased her neck, bringing thoughts she tried to block from her mind. They had spent all week together and he hadn't made a single advance since the day of the picnic. Brenna had waited expectantly for his next move, forming silent speeches in her mind for when the moment came. But nothing happened and her expectation turned to frustration. She wanted him to make a pass. She wanted his lips on hers, his hands molding the curves of her body. She was confused and irritated by her inability to make sense of her feelings for this man, more emotional about it than she had ever dreamed possible. One minute she wanted him to do something so she could spurn his attempt; the next minute she wanted him to do something so she could be in his arms once more, could experience what her body told her she wanted. Either way she would lose him, so she kept silent.

"Now, bring it back and try to slide the club under the ball for a good chip shot." His hands tightened over hers as he swung the club in a slow arc, stopping just behind the ball. Stepping back, he motioned for her to play the ball on her own. She tried to remember everything he had said and brought the club around in what she thought was a good swing, only to miss the ball completely.

"I give up, Marc," she said, exasperated. "I know you love this game, but it just doesn't make any sense to me."

"What do you mean?"

"I've watched tournaments on television and I've seen the players' enormous concentration, but to me chasing a ball around a big lawn is just a little bit short of insanity."

Marc's hands came to rest on her shoulders as he turned her around to face him. His lips quirked into a smile as she tried to explain herself.

"I don't know why men would compete against

106

each other in a sport where they don't even know how the other player is doing until hours later."

"In the first place, a player competes more against the course and his own record than against another player. But I understand what you're saying. Just remember, though, when I buy you an expensive gift or two, that this silly little game is probably what paid for it."

"I don't really mean it's silly—I mean I have no aptitude for it."

"I wonder what your best sport is?" he murmured, pulling her into his arms, his lips resting on her forehead to send her temperature shooting higher than it already was.

Brenna's arms circled his waist, the club dropping to the ground, forgotten in the rush of feelings she was experiencing. Excitement raced through her system, washing it clean of everything except his nearness. Her lips unerringly found the hollow of his throat and she kissed his sun-warmed skin. He froze immediately, stiffening as he pulled away from her to stand staring out at the fairway.

"Marc?" Her voice quivered as she tried to fathom the thoughts behind those dark brown eyes. Had he thought she wanted more than a kiss? She blushed a becoming peach as she realized that he probably thought she was willing to become what he had wanted and now was tired of her and her childish ways. He had proven his point the best way of all—by refusing what he thought she was offering.

"Sorry, Brenna, but I'm not going to play your games unless you mean to deliver." He bent and picked up the balls, slipping them into a side pocket of the bright fawn and brown golf bag. "When you're ready, let me know, but don't play any games with me meanwhile."

"Is that what you thought I was doing?"

"Wasn't it?" His eyes narrowed, taking in her small heart-shaped face, her eyes bright with barely held back tears. "You know yourself that all you wanted was a kiss. If I had tried to push you any further you would have backed off with some speech, no doubt already written in your pretty little head, about morality and the sanctity of engagements."

"Yes," she admitted, raising her chin just a little in defiance. "But it would have been no worse than the speech I would have given myself. I want more than you have to offer."

"I've offered everything you want except the ring, Brenna. Don't forget that."

"That's everything," she said quietly, turning back toward the house. It was time to leave.

"Where are you going?" His voice was sharp, halting her in her tracks.

"I've got to leave now. Perhaps there's another job waiting for me. I should be working, not just being with you."

"I'm paying for this time, Brenna. And don't worry, I can afford it. I own half interest in a restaurant chain and I'm in partnership with an electronics firm here in Phoenix." He watched her expression change to surprise and his eyes narrowed.

"Does that make a difference? Will it change your no to a yes?"

"I didn't know you did anything other than play golf professionally." Her quiet dignity came through in her stance and cool, calm eyes. "But no—I can't be bought, Marc."

He sighed ruefully. "I never thought you could." He raked her body with his glance. "That's why I'm building a house here. I intend to make Phoenix my winter home. But I suppose the gossips have already told you that." He bent to pick up the golf bag, slinging it over his shoulder as he had undoubtedly done many times before.

"Yes, I did hear something about it. But I was hoping you'd confirm it."

"Consider it confirmed. Now, let's go have a drink on the patio. The sunset should be putting on a stellar performance any time now and I'd hate to miss the show."

He was suddenly all charm again, the stiffness gone as if it had never existed. Brenna let a sigh escape her lips as they walked to the canvas covered patio. Her emotions had done nothing but ride a roller coaster ever since she had met Marc. She wondered when it would end but didn't want to think about it. Life without Marc would be a living death and she knew it. Love had finally burst into her life and it was the most painful emotion of all.

She took a deep breath. First things first. Her relationship with Marc had nothing to do with Lee, except that it showed her she could never marry a man she didn't love to the fullest. The next step, then, was to break up with Lee, to tell him her feelings and allow him his out. He would be angry and hurt, but he'd get over it and go about his orderly life within weeks, she was sure.

Oh, Marc, her heart cried, why can't you love me the way I love you?

There was no answer, just a feeling of despair.

"I hereby resolve," Brenna said out loud to the reflection in her bedroom mirror, "not to allow Marc's remarks to hurt me again!"

She adjusted the bodice of her dress one more time. It was pale green, with a demure neckline and small capped sleeves. The hem fell in soft folds around her knees, swishing delightfully as she walked. She hoped she resembled a schoolteacher in it, having bought it originally for her first interview with the school board. Now she was wearing it to impress Marc. After this past week she would need all the armor she could find to repel Marc's advances before he made them. She had a feeling that if she let down her guard just once it would be too late, for she never would find the courage to say no to something she wanted so terribly. Brenna touched her eyelashes with mascara, then blotted the pale orange lipstick from her mouth. That was all the makeup she would need if they were going to look at land again today.

Marc opened the door just as Brenna pulled into the driveway. He looked tall and lithe, masterful but controlled. His white shirt and apricot pants were a perfect foil for his tanned skin and dark hair. The mirrored sunglasses hid his eyes again, making him look like the perfect image of a jet-setter. Suddenly Brenna felt uncomfortable. If he touched her today she knew she couldn't resist. Her stomach churned, giving her an inkling of what the battle before her would be like. Her confused thoughts had beset her all week, yet she hadn't come any closer to knowing what he really wanted from their relationship.

"Good morning. You're punctual as usual. I like that," he said amicably, folding his long, lean form into the car seat. He shut the door and turned to her. "You're looking very nice—like a nun trying to remember her vows."

"Why don't you leave me alone?" Brenna snapped while turning pink with embarrassment. There went her calm, cool front! She apologized immediately. "I'm sorry. I didn't mean to snap at you so early in the morning. It's just that you seem to enjoy provoking me."

Marc smiled. "I do enjoy it. You're always so quick to rise to the bait, never taking it as conversational banter."

"Should I?" Most of the people she knew wouldn't know his kind of conversational banter from a hole in the ground.

His face, or what she could see of it, turned serious. Those mirror glasses were disconcerting, hiding the most important part of him.

"No, not really. I suppose I've become jaded. In

my circle everyone says what they don't mean and acts the way they don't want to and all to put up a good front. After a while you forget what you really feel and only live the front."

He was more relaxed today than he had been all week and Brenna relaxed, too. "That sounds like a pretty cynical outlook," she said, not exactly sure she knew what he was referring to until a picture of Lee flashed into her mind. Lee did that all the time, yet until now she hadn't wanted to recognize it for what it was—phony. They had hardly seen each other in the weeks since the night of the cocktail party. He had been busy traveling and escorting an out-of-town client and Brenna had been busy with her work. . . .

Brenna was lost in thought until Marc's hand on her shoulder startled her back to reality.

"Turn right at the stop sign," he said, leaving his hand where it was. She could feel his warmth flooding through her, turning her resolution into water. Before her willpower flowed completely away she grasped his wrist and forced his hand away, ignoring his husky chuckle. The road climbed higher, turning into a dirt road as it continued to twist upward. Finally they reached the top of the hill and the road ended.

Marc was out of the car before Brenna had turned off the engine. He walked to the small crest and stood looking down, his image outlined against the next hill. He looked like a Greek god in an open-air temple as the wind ruffled his black hair. One impatient hand ran through the thick tangles, pushing it out of his eyes. He turned slowly, surveying the rest of the summit.

Brenna left the car slowly. The breeze gently whipped her dress about her slim legs and forced the material against her breasts. She stood beside Marc as they both gazed over the terrain in silence.

The top of the hill covered about five acres in all, sloping down on three sides with a cliff on the fourth. A natural rise in one corner made it easy for Brenna to imagine a wide, spacious hacienda sitting on that spot, with a pool and a green sloping lawn. There wasn't a house in sight.

"It's beautiful," Brenna whispered.

"So are you," Marc responded, his voice equally soft. "Do you like it?"

"Oh, yes," she breathed.

"How do you see it? Tell me."

"A white Spanish-style hacienda over there." She pointed toward the rise. "A pool here, and green sloping lawns covering the rest of it."

"With small green flags sticking out of the little holes?" he teased.

She laughed, nodding her head. "Definitely!"

He held out his hand and she took it. "Then come along and see my living room."

They walked slowly to the rise and sat down. "Now, show me the house," he demanded, his arms resting on bent knees, his whole body totally relaxed.

"The living room should be over there, where that

yucca is. It should be big, with windows on two sides, a tiled floor, and a cathedral ceiling. Across a tiled hall there should be a library, which would double as your study when you have to work at home. It should have a fireplace with large floor-to-ceiling windows on either side. Back there is the dining room and behind it the kitchen." She turned slightly. "Now, over there should be the bedroom—or bedrooms. How many do you want?"

"One is enough for a start." Humor tinged his voice.

"What about company? And family?"

"The only company I want is you. And you certainly won't be sleeping in another bed."

She ignored that last remark. "In that case my family and I can't visit you," she said imperiously, her nose in the air in mock disdain. "My family needs five bedrooms, at least!"

His glasses came off to show eyes wide with shock. "Five bedrooms for a family? How many of you are there?"

"I have four brothers and three sisters, plus my mother and father," she answered.

His jaw dropped and he was left speechless.

Brenna couldn't keep a straight face any longer and they both collapsed on the ground in giggles. Once the laughter died away they became very still, eyes locked.

Marc turned over on his side, resting his head on one hand. "Welcome to my bedroom." His voice was husky and it excited her almost as much as the hand that softly roamed the contours of her stomach and ribs, stopping just short of her firm, uptilted breasts. Brenna's breath stopped and she was certain he could read the naked desire in her eyes as they stared luminously into his.

He bent his head to stop just a warm breath away from hers. His tongue slowly drew a pattern on her lips and she opened them readily, wanting him to stop his teasing and complete the kiss.

She wrapped her arms about his neck, waiting . . . waiting . . . hoping he wouldn't stiffen and pull away. Her hands slipped inside his collar, stroking and feeling the heated skin against her palms and wanting to feel more, more. Whenever she was around him her emotions seemed to go haywire and all decorous thoughts scattered in the warm desert wind.

"If you keep that up we'll be back to where we were last week. And I'm not sure you're ready yet." Marc nuzzled her neck, his hands roaming her body as if to memorize every curve.

Brenna couldn't move, couldn't pull herself together enough to disguise the impact he made on her.

With a low groan he turned away and flung a handful of scrub grass to the wind. "Get up, Brenna," he said harshly, his control finally slipping. "If you stay there I just might take advantage. I'm not used to denying myself what I want."

Brenna rose to a sitting position slowly, a small smile playing about her lips. So he *had* been as affected as she was! Her hand ran down his spine in an intimate caress, confident of his restraint until he turned to look at her once more. What she saw frightened her more than anything she had ever seen. Raw, animal hunger shone from his dark eyes, freezing her into stillness. He was a leopard claiming ownership of his mate, provocative and extremely dangerous.

"When are you kissing Lee good-bye?"

Brenna's mind ran in circles. Lee? She forced herself back to reality. She hadn't been able to talk to Lee since Marc had arrived back in town, but she knew she would have to. She nibbled on her finger. "Tonight . . ."

"You're still seeing him then?"

"Not really, but I will this evening."

Marc grasped her arm, almost bruising her with his hard grip. "I don't like the idea of you seeing him alone. I'll come over."

"No, I can handle this. The least I can do is give him a private explanation," Brenna said simply.

Marc sighed. "I guess you're right. I just don't like the idea of you being alone with him. Who knows what the fool might do?"

Her hand rested on his arm, her heart warm with his concern. "He won't do anything, but I owe him that much, Marc. Our plans were made long ago and he deserves to hear about any changes in our relationship without your presence."

Marc's grin was lopsided with a tinge of self-derision. "You've been safe with him all this time. I guess once more won't matter." His hand covered hers and the look he gave her sent warmth flooding through her body. "He was a fool not to take what you have to offer. I wouldn't have waited a minute longer than necessary."

"Then why are you waiting now?" she teased, loving the feel of his calloused thumb rubbing against the palm of her hand.

"Only because I want you to have enough time to get your life together. When you move in with me I don't want any other guy hanging around. I may not be a pillar of society, but I do have my own code."

A frown marred her forehead and his hand came up to smooth the wrinkles from her brow. She had to face the question now. Was she really the type of girl who could move in with a man without benefit of marriage? Brenna knew the answer, but hated to admit it to herself or him.

"I can't move in with you, Marc. I just can't."

"What do you mean? I thought it was all decided."

"You decided for me. I've said no before," she stated firmly. "I have to break up with Lee because I realize now that what I thought was love was really just a kind of friendship. My breaking up with him has nothing to do with you. Lee may not be the right man for me, but someday there will be a man for me to marry."

"Marriage!" he scoffed derisively. "A commitment to be committed! What the devil does that prove?"

She shook her head slowly, not knowing the answer he sought. "It doesn't prove anything, but it does mean loving someone and staying with them through good and bad. I need to make that kind of commitment." Her eyes silently begged him to understand, but he was immune to her plea.

"You were willing to make that commitment with Lee, even when it would have been a failure, Brenna."

"I was willing to try. That's more than you're ready to do."

He was silent for a long moment before answering. "I was taught long ago by my mother never to trust in marriage any more than you can trust in family. She used me as a weapon against my father until he couldn't take any more and left for good. Then she dropped me off at the welfare board to be taken care of in homes all across Indiana. I never saw her again until I made a name for myself in golf," he said bitterly, one hand unconsciously clenching into a fist. "Then she suddenly wanted her darling son back so he could give her the money she needed. She'd lost her looks by then and men weren't interested in her anymore."

"And you think that's an example of love and commitment?" Brenna asked softly.

"It's closer to the norm than the lifestyle you grew up with, with your parents and seven brothers and sisters. You're very naive, Brenna. I see relationships like mine with my mother every day, in business and on the golf circuit. Marriage isn't a commitment, just a way of locking up someone else's money and life in a neat little box until one of you gets tired of such a confined way of living."

Brenna's hand left his back to rest on her lap. What was the point? He would never understand. "I'm sorry, Marc. I still think marriage is something very special."

Marc stood to impatiently brush the red earth from his pants before walking down the hillside. "So, the lady believes in the sanctity of marriage!" he sneered. "I wonder if you really know *what* you believe! Do you still read fairy tales, too, Brenna?"

"Only for fun." She stood and smoothed the back of her dress with nervous hands. Her heart thudded with the pain of his words, but for the first time she was calm in his presence. "I know that whoever I marry will understand my need for freedom to work or think or do as I please. Just as I'll try to understand his wants and needs." Her voice was gentle, but it held deep conviction.

"Does that mean that either of you can play around and neither one will get hurt?"

"It means neither one will want to play around or try to hurt the other."

"And you'll hand him that virtue of yours on a silver platter to tie him to you."

She nodded slowly, hoping he wouldn't see the tears of dejection that filled her eyes. "If that's the way you want to see it."

"If . . ." He turned quickly, staring at her with a coldness that stabbed her like a thousand tiny icicles.

"I don't know what you expect from me, Marc."

His hands were clenched at his sides and she

119

wondered distantly why he should be so angry; there were plenty of other women willing to live by his rules.

"You know what I think, Brenna? I think I could talk you into making love, but you wouldn't live with me. Talk about hypocritical! But you and I both know that fifteen minutes ago I could probably have taken you and you wouldn't have put one obstacle in my way!"

"I just know what I can live with and what I can't. I can't tolerate the idea of my family finding out I was living with a man without marriage. It would kill my parents, lower my self-esteem, and set a bad example for my brothers and sisters, all of whom mean a great deal to me."

Marc shook his head in disbelief. "Propriety seems to be the key word, Brenna. Don't do anything others may not like." He looked at her with disgust and it felt like a sharp blade slipping between her ribs. "At least I've always let you know where I stand, Brenna. And that's more than I can say for you. One minute you're melting in my arms, ready to make love, then the next minute you're telling me your family responsibilities won't let you. What an excuse!" His mouth twisted into a semblance of a smile. "You've set a price on yourself and that price is too high. You just don't know what you're asking for when you ask for marriage, Brenna."

His words hit her like a slap and she reeled with the impact. A whistling breeze filled the silence as they both stood like marble statues on the crest of the hill. A faraway horn honked and Marc suddenly jumped into action, ignoring the pain in her eyes. "Let's go," he ordered, turning to face the car.

She held out her hand, imploring him for she didn't know what. "Marc, please, wait."

"No!" he threw over his shoulder. "I may say something I might regret if we don't get out of here. Now!"

Brenna followed him down the slope and silently entered the intimate confines of the car. Her heart ached with unshed tears. Where was her cool, calm self now? Was it gone forever? Would she ever be on solid ground again? Somehow she knew that no matter what happened in the future she would never be the same again. And with that thought came a cloak of depression that made the sunny day a dark and terrifying night. . . .

She had been a fool! She should have said, "Yes, yes, yes!" Her mind couldn't conceive of the emptiness that would follow her through life without Marc. Brenna's hand shook as she dialed Marc's number. She hadn't been home fifteen minutes when she realized that to have Marc on his terms was better than never having him at all.

"Hello?" a sultry female voice answered, just a hint of humor in the tone, as if she had just been chuckling at a good joke.

Brenna froze instinctively and her breath stopped. She knew that voice. "I think you have a silent admirer, darling," the other woman cooed, and a second later Marc's voice came through the wires.

"Hello?" He hesitated, waiting for an answer.

"Hello?" He sounded irritated. "Brenna, is that you?" Brenna's finger slowly went to the disconnect button, though she continued to hold the receiver next to her ear. She heard the short, dull click and knew she had cut the connection. Slowly, she placed the receiver back on the hook.

Chapter Seven

Brenna moved around the apartment like a robot as she did her chores that evening, her mind consumed with putting one foot in front of the other just to get the vacuum cleaner from here to there. She had emptied the trash, changed the sheets on her bed, done the laundry in the laundromat down the street, and even folded all the clothes, including Carol's. Now the last job was almost done. The machine wheezed to a stop, telling her the bag was full. Blast! Couldn't Carol do anything? It was all Brenna could do not to throw the machine out the door. But another part of her remained calm. Too calm.

Carol had come in early that evening, quickly changed clothes and left to meet a few friends for a new horror movie. Though she'd noticed Brenna's preoccupation, she had chalked it up to tiredness. Carol knew Brenna had carried a heavy schedule that week. Besides, Carol thought all engaged girls got jittery.

Brenna wrapped the cord around the stem of the cleaner, deciding that she had done enough for the evening. When the doorbell rang, for one blessed moment her heart stopped in anticipation, hoping it was Marc. But it began beating again when she glanced at the clock and realized that it must be Lee, as punctual as ever.

She grumbled under her breath as she slipped the vacuum cleaner into the closet, almost slamming the door on her fingers. She fervently wished she had set this inevitable meeting for another time, when she could have handled it better. Her parting with Marc this afternoon was still very much in her mind and her entire being balked at trying to discuss anything with anyone else. But there was no way out of it now.

Lee's kiss was perfunctory. He strolled casually into the apartment, surveying its neatness like a prospective bridegroom buying a bride, nodding while silently grading her efforts before he sat down on the small couch. Brenna had turned the radio on earlier and the station filled the room with soft, sultry music. Quickly she switched it off, leaving a silence that seemed louder than the music had been.

"What's so urgent, darling? I'm supposed to be doing some land research for Mr. Chapman, so I'm afraid I can't stay long." Lee's arm was thrown casually across the back of the couch as he crossed his legs and stretched out. "Get me a drink, will you? Scotch and soda will do. Ice please."

It took all the control Brenna could muster to walk to the small cabinet against the wall and take out the necessary bottles to mix his drink, eyeing him through narrowed lashes all the time. She threw a few ice cubes in a glass, added Scotch, then the soda, before holding it out to Lee, almost spilling the contents in the process and not caring.

Lee's eyes flickered; he was obviously irritated at her manner, but apparently he decided to hold his peace for the moment. He took a sip, looking very satisfied with the results of her labor.

"Have you been driving that golfer around?" he asked as if he really didn't care.

"Yes." Brenna's voice was sharp as she took a long, deep breath. This wasn't the time to vent her frustrations. It wasn't Lee's fault that her entire world had rocked on its axis today.

Lee raised an eyebrow, inviting her to begin, while he sipped his drink. Obviously he wanted her to come right to the point and that irritated her even more than his imperious order for the drink.

Brenna took a deep breath. "Lee, when did we say we were going to get married?"

He frowned, perplexed. "When I thought I was established enough in business to take on the debts and responsibilities involved in having a wife," he answered, sitting a little straighter.

Finally aware that this was a serious conversation, he patted the cushion next to him. "Come sit down and tell me what's troubling you."

125

Brenna took the small chair across from him, ignoring his flash of irritation at her choice.

"When will that be? This year? Next year? Five years from now?" she persisted.

"When I say it is," he answered imperiously, his full mouth thinning.

"And do I have anything to say about it?"

"Is that what this is all about?" Lee asked with a smirk. "What is it, darling? Are you eager for the marriage bed? Do you want equal time? It's all right with me as long as we agree on this first."

Agreeing meant saying yes to his date, not hers, and Brenna sat back in her chair. Finally she had lost all feelings of guilt for doing what she was about to do.

"I see," she murmured softly, understanding more than he had given her credit for. Slowly she twisted around in her chair, tucking her feet under her. At last she was able to rectify a situation that never should have been. This hurt far less than if she had begun something with Marc and carried it too far to go back.

"Thank you for honoring me with your proposal, Lee, but you deserve someone else—someone who could live with your rules. We aren't suited."

His face was a study, she thought. Shock, disbelief, anger, and cunning flitted across his handsome features as she watched him closely, wondering how she had ever found anything in him to like. Not only was he never satisfied with her behavior, but he had put her down every chance he got. Why hadn't she seen it before? She had, a little voice told her, but she had tried to ignore it in her desire to be wanted. Independence was a wonderful thing to talk about, but it didn't give you a feeling of closeness to see you through life.

"I don't believe you, Brenna." Lee brought her back to the conversation. "Is it that golfer? Is that it?"

Her face gave her away and Lee's grin became a leer. "You think that just because he's interested in you he'd offer marriage?" He shook his head, taking joy in her misery. "He'd take you to bed, but that's as far as his commitment would go. You're not his type."

Commitment. The word brought back the scene on the hill with Marc. Tears of sorrow burned Brenna's eyes.

But her humiliation receded as she stared through tear-laden lashes at the man she had pledged to marry. Her anger slowly rose to the surface, making her aware of her feelings for the first time that day.

"I don't recall asking you what type I am and I'm not at all interested in what you think of my morals. Luckily they belong to me and aren't up for scrutiny," she said coldly.

But Lee was angry, too. "You used to care about what I thought. Apparently you were putting on an act in order to catch a husband."

"Perhaps you're right." Brenna stood, her action dismissing him from her life. "We're both lucky we found this out now, Lee."

Lee wasn't to be thwarted so easily. Reaching for his drink, he downed it quickly, then placed the glass back on the table with a thud.

"So you like those macho types, do you? I treated you too nicely. I respected you too much. I thought that anything else would shock you. But I was wrong, wasn't I?" He stood, swaying slowly. The adrenaline had pumped the alcohol through his system more quickly than usual. "I should have treated you like what you are." He nodded, his eyes bright. "Oh, yes. I saw how he held you in his arms that night on the dance floor. I knew he was making suggestive comments in your ear, and you ate it up, didn't you?"

"Then why didn't you stop him?"

She had silently begged Lee to intervene that night, but he had continued to sit complacently and watch.

Lee shrugged, taking a step closer, as if to come around the coffee table. "I thought you could handle yourself. I wanted his account if I could get it. It never dawned on me that you'd be so taken in by that type of behavior. Goes to show how wrong I was!"

He reached out and grasped her wrist, snapping her into his arms before she could protest. His hands were punishing on her soft skin as they trailed a path under her shirt and along her spine, bringing tears to her eyes. She struggled, but her arms were pinned to her sides.

"Let me go!" she cried, but his lips came down in a cruel kiss. She squirmed, finally managing to release his hold, and took several steps back. She wiped her hand across her bruised lips, the fire sparking from her eyes telling him of her anger and disgust. No one had a right to handle her that way! No one!

"Get out, Lee, and never come back." She practically growled the words. "Now!"

"I'll get even with you for this, Brenna." He took a deep breath and walked stiffly to the door. He opened it before turning to look back at her once more. "If the newspapers get hold of your 'meetings' with the famous Marc Lawter, you can be sure your reputation will be in shreds. He only dates girls who know the score, so you can guess what people will think of you." His sneer was enough to send a shiver down Brenna's spine. "You'll be sorry for this, Brenna. You'll be sorry." The door slammed hard, tilting the small decorative mirror on the wall. Then he was gone.

Brenna stood still, her shaking hands holding the back of the chair as if it were a lifeline. At the closing bang of the door she slowly sank into the soft cushions. Sobs came in uncontrollable gasps. Within two short weeks her life had been completely turned around. Now she was further away from that elusive feeling called happiness than she had ever been. At least two weeks ago she had had an illusion, but now she had nothing. Nothing.

The call she had expected came later in the evening. Bob, the dispatcher at work, informed her that her services were no longer needed by Mr. Lawter. The young man sounded puzzled, but didn't ask questions, and Brenna was glad, for she didn't know the answers. Her hand groped to place the telephone back on the hook in the dark as she continued to stare up at the ceiling. Her eyes were dry now, but they refused to close. It was going to be a long night.

The days dragged wretchedly and Brenna's spirits dragged with them. Carol watched with concern as Brenna moved around the apartment and work in slow motion. She had lost weight and pale purple bruises circled her once sparkling green eyes, yet she laughed and joked with friends as if nothing was wrong. When the girls got together Brenna was there, cutting up with the rest of them. When a new horror movie came to town Brenna was one of the first to notice and make plans for them to go.

As the weeks passed, more weight slowly dropped from Brenna's slim frame.

"In another few days you'll be able to rent yourself out to medical students as the only living corpse," Carol joked one morning as they sat across the breakfast table from each other. Carol was devouring frozen waffles while Brenna nursed a lukewarm cup of coffee.

Brenna shrugged, uncaring. "I might decide to go into modeling." She stared into her cup and watched the cream congeal.

"I didn't know you were that attached to Lee, Brenna." Carol's voice was low and full of compassion. "I'm sorry it didn't work out."

Brenna's head came up, her eyes blank. "What?"

Carol stood to clear her dishes. Her voice was exasperated. "All right, so you don't want to talk about it. I understand." She dumped the dishes in the sink and turned on the hot water. "What I don't understand is your reaction to all this. He was cute and a go-getter, but he certainly wasn't a man to tear your heart out and leave you bleeding. Lee hated messes!"

Comprehension dawned at last and Brenna's face broke into a smile, which grew wider as she burst into laughter. It was the first time she had laughed spontaneously since her breakup with Marc.

"I fail to see anything funny in my condolences," Carol said.

"I'm sorry, Carol." Brenna wiped her eyes. "It's just that Lee is the farthest thing from my mind. In fact, I'd forgotten about him completely until you mentioned his name!"

"You're kidding!" Carol stared at her roommate as if she had just grown another head, sending Brenna into a fit of laughter again.

"No, I'm not. He and I were never right for each other. I knew it even when I said I'd marry him, but I went ahead anyway, hoping for something to happen that never did. I never loved him, Carol. But I wanted him to love me. Selfish, wasn't it?"

"Then what on earth is this whole thing about?" Carol questioned, now thoroughly confused. "You've been moping around here like you've lost your will to live and all you can tell me is that Lee is the only thing that's *not* bothering you!"

A small light began to flicker in Brenna's eyes as

she digested the truth of Carol's words. "You're right—I have been moping around for no good reason," she said grimly. "I was paid in full for what I did to Lee, and now it's time to stop. No man is important enough to mope over. Especially him!" She stood and practically marched out of the kitchen, leaving her perplexed roommate staring at her retreating back.

Carol shook her head. "What is she talking about if not Lee?" she asked aloud. Suddenly the light dawned and for the first time in weeks Carol understood the reason for the depression Brenna had been going through. Oh, *him!* she exclaimed to herself. Now she *really* had something to worry about!

Brenna continued to work and play hard, but no more would she mope over a lady-killer who thought that all he had to do was ask to receive his fair share of maidens! He could drop dead, she told herself. Her Irish heritage wasn't a timid thing and once her period of mourning was over it was over. She had learned her lesson well and without coming away too badly scarred. The few mementos that Marc had left behind didn't show; they were all memories that she could keep hidden, to die in the darkness of her mind.

She read in the paper that night that Marc Lawter was in Phoenix for the weekend, closely watching the building of his dream house. She remembered that piece of land high on the hill before she realized where her memories were heading and quickly shut them off.

A few days later she read that Marc Lawter was in

Palm Springs for the Bob Hope Open. He came in third, which didn't seem to please him, if his picture meant anything. But the lovely blonde at his side couldn't have looked happier if he had placed first.

Brenna wished wholeheartedly that she had the strength to give up reading the newspaper! Every night she swore she wouldn't open the sports section and every night it managed to fall into her hands. Every night her eyes searched the gray pages for news of the man she pretended to hate.

Finally anger came to her rescue again and she shoved the newspaper to the floor, promising herself once more that it would be the last time she would ever read that particular section.

Her decision melted as the next day wore on . . . and the next newspaper was delivered.

Chapter Eight

August was the hottest month in Arizona. The temperature reached a melting 115 degrees in the shade even before the fiery sun was completely overhead. Thank goodness for the low humidity, Brenna thought. She wiped her damp brow with the back of her wrist as she sat back and surveyed her mother's version of the old-fashioned Victory garden. Rain had been scarcer this year than usual and even though the garden had been watered daily the plants looked as if nothing could revive them.

Everywhere Brenna turned the tough Tucson soil was holding what should have been range grass, but instead resembled tufts of dry hay. Brenna had been pulling weeds for hours, the work a necessary therapy for her dented emotions. Her eyes locked onto a struggling patch of radishes, but her thoughts were far away. She was with Marc as they had been on the hilltop outside Phoenix, his eyes smiling into hers, turning her blood into molten lava. His hands held her breast, the rough calluses sending a feeling of bliss . . . Stop it! she told herself.

She stood and dusted the knees of her worn and faded jeans. As soon as she set the sprinkler up she would head for the house. Her stomach growled, telling her it was time to eat.

The house was large, rambling, stuccoed, and in need of whitewash. Her parents had bought it when their second son, Tommy, was born. Since then a wing had been added here, a room there, until it looked like a caricature of the original design. But inside those walls was as much loving warmth as could be crammed into a palace. Brenna was glad that she had decided to spend the weekend with them. She had been away too long.

Brenna opened the screen door and wiped her feet on the well-worn doormat. "Where's Dad, Mom?" she asked, washing her hands under the kitchen tap, then sitting down at the table. "Has he had his lunch or is he coming in?" she questioned as she bit into a tuna sandwich rich with homemade mayonnaise.

Her mother poured herself a cup of coffee, then sat down opposite Brenna.

"One of the children will take it out to him in a little while. He's up at number two pasture." Her sharp green eyes gave Brenna a concerned once-over. "Unless you'd like to talk to him."

Brenna nodded her head, thankful that her mouth was too full to answer. That was exactly what she needed to do. Her dad had known all the answers when she was young; he couldn't have changed too much in the past few years.

"His lunch is packed and ready, over on the counter. Take Poco and ride out." Her mother's hand covered Brenna's for an instant, giving a slight squeeze. "By the way, it's nice to have you home."

Brenna's eyes filled with love. "How could you tell I was gone with this motley crew around?" she tried to joke.

"Each one of you is special, like the pieces of the jigsaw puzzles you used to put together when you were younger. The one you always worry over is the piece that's missing."

Brenna walked over to her mother, giving a bear hug to the smaller woman. "Your pieces will always be coming home, Mom. This is where they fit best."

"No," her mother said emphatically. "They fit where they find love." She looked up at her daughter's face. "And that's the way it should be. It was that way for your father and me and I hope it will be the same for each of you." She dusted her hands off in a nervous gesture. "Now go and take your father his lunch. He's probably starved."

The ride out to the pasture was exhilarating. It had been ages since Brenna had ridden a horse and she'd forgotten how free it felt. The hot wind painted her cheeks with color. The open terrain allowed her eyes to wander in all directions and with each darting glance came a feeling of familiarity, of oneness with nature. She had been born out here and it was as much a part of her as it was of her parents. How had she stood living in Phoenix these past four years? She thought of the hill where Marc had taken her and knew that half the appeal of it was that it reminded her of home.

Her father was on the other side of the barbed-wire fence and, with reckless abandon, Brenna dug her heels into the old horse and leaned forward, ready to jump the low tangle of wire. Her father must have heard her coming, for he stood and waved his hand in the air as he shouted a welcome. They jumped and as she reined the panting horse to a stop just short of her father her face was wreathed in a smile, laughter bubbling from her lips.

"What's the matter, Dad? Did you think I wouldn't make it?" she teased, jumping to the ground.

"Oh, I had no doubt that *you'd* make it—I was worried about old Poco. He hasn't had that much exercise in a long while." His hand caught the reins and looped them over one of the fence posts before he turned to take the large plastic sack from Brenna. "I thought you were your mother for a minute, with that hair streaming behind you and an expression of pure joy on your face."

They seated themselves in the shade of a twisted mesquite tree. After having seen him yesterday for the first time in six months, that old feeling was still there, as if she had never left home. Her father had always been the one she had gone to in times of trouble and he had never failed to provide calm, understanding solutions to her problems.

"Mom?" Brenna exclaimed incredulously. "I can't imagine her riding out here like that!"

Her dad smiled, lifting his weather-beaten hat to wipe his forehead with the sleeve of his shirt. "Who do you think used to bring me lunch before you kids came along?"

"Really?"

He nodded. "Really!" he mocked. "She was just a child of nineteen then, and as full of life and mischief as you are now." His eyes held a dreamy, faraway look and a small smile tugged at the corner of his mouth as he remembered.

"Were you very much in love?" she questioned softly.

"Oh, yes. I thought I wasn't going to live *without* her and she thought I wasn't good enough to live *with* her!" he retorted.

"How did you ever get together?"

"I was good with words in those days. I painted a picture of how it would be when I stepped out of her life and she didn't like what she saw." He snapped his fingers. "It was that quick and she told me we were getting married." He chuckled. "At the time I was twenty-two and didn't have a dime in my pocket. I was hoping we could come to a more amicable solution, but . . ." He unwrapped his sandwich. "I had to have been the luckiest man alive. Still am."

"Did you ever want to . . . I mean, did you and Mom . . . ?" She stopped, frustrated with the words that were coming out all wrong.

"Of course I wanted to," her dad stated calmly, as if he was answering a question about the weather.

"But in those days it wasn't the thing. Besides, I wanted everything that went along with loving her: the wedding, the children—everything. I wouldn't have been even half a man if I had taken what I wanted and she wouldn't have been worth having." He popped the cap off his soft drink and took a deep swallow. "But how about you? Is that what you want? The house, the trimmings, the babies? Or do you want a life with a man who places you second or third in his life?" he asked, his sharp eyes seeing more than she wanted to show.

Brenna sighed, glad it was out in the open. How well her father could read her mind! "I don't know what I want, Dad. But he knew he wanted me without benefit of the 'trappings.'"

"And you wanted it that way, too?"

Brenna didn't answer immediately. "I'm not sure what I want."

"Yes, you are. You're sure you want him, but you're not sure you want the consequences that go along with that decision."

"How did you know?" She looked up, startled.

His eyes twinkled. "Times may have changed, honey, but the problems remain the same." He patted her hand. "And you're right to worry about afterward. That's the part you have to live with." He hesitated, giving her hand a squeeze. "Sometimes I wish I had a magic formula I could pull out and give to each of you kids so nothing would hurt any of you. But it's impossible. The only thing I can do is give you my guidance up to a certain point, then allow you to grow your own way. You won't grow if I put you in a jar. You have to be free to make decisions—right and wrong ones—so you know better the next time." He sighed heavily. "This decision is yours to make. You already know what the consequences would be for you, just as you know how your mother and I would feel. The only other person you really have to figure out is the guy." He looked at her, his eyes delving deeply into her soul. "Is he worth what your conscience will put you through?"

She looked down, plucking a blade of dry grass. "I don't know, Dad." Her fingers felt the razor-sharp edge of the grass. "But it doesn't matter now. I'll probably never see him again, unless I go to him." Her chin rose determinedly. "And I'll never do that."

"I take it that this young man is not Lee?" her father asked drily.

Brenna chuckled, aware of her father's dislike for Lee. "No, it's not Lee. I'm not sure how I ever got into that situation."

"I'm not, either. You're too impetuous and fun-loving for someone as stuffy as he is. I never did like his type," he said calmly. "But it seems you went from the frying pan into the fire. This new one sounds far more dangerous!"

Brenna had made up her mind. "He was," she said slowly. "But he's not anymore. I don't think I could live in that sort of situation and be happy."

Her father pulled out a crumpled pack of cigarettes and lit one. After the first drag he let it dangle from his mouth. He fit the image of the typical cowboy in his jeans and plaid shirt, his eyes permanently squinted from the sun and smoke.

Suddenly Brenna felt a wave of love for this man who had fathered and reared her and wondered how he could ever have put up with all the shenanigans she and her brothers had pulled while growing up. She leaned over and gave him a squeeze. "I love you, you know that?"

"Keep telling me, honey. I like to hear it as much as the next man."

They laughed, then he became serious once again. "You know that feeling you get when you look at someone you think you love?" he asked and she nodded her head. "Well, a good marriage is one that grows—that feeling spreads and changes into others that are deeper and more meaningful. But every once in a while, years later, you can look at that person and still want to hug them and tell them how much they mean to you. That's a good marriage."

"Did you know from the start?"

He laughed. "I did, but I don't think your mother was too sure about us for a while."

"Why do you say that?"

"Because she always had an overnighter packed and hidden away in the closet." He stood and dusted off his jeans before he looked over at her, his eyes twinkling once more. "I don't mind telling you, it kept me on my toes for a few years!"

Brenna sighed, standing to collect the litter left from lunch. "I wonder if I'll ever feel that way."

Her father groaned in mock despair. "What did your mother and I ever do to you children? One son believes he may be divorcing before he's even married and the other doesn't believe she'll ever make it to the altar!"

Laughter bubbled from her lips. It was true; Tommy was the worrier, yet here she was doing the same thing!

"Poor doubting Thomas!" she laughed. "He's so cautious he can't even see that Janie is perfect for him!"

"He will, as soon as he breaks up with her. One week of not having her around is all he'll need before he goes running back to set a date, no questions asked," her father responded. "The problem is that Janie is there to cook and clean for him. He doesn't realize just how much a part of his life she is."

Brenna's eyes were large as saucers. "My goodness, are they living together? I never thought Janie would do that!"

"No, but she spends every free moment over there, so Tom says. He's gotten in the habit of having her do for him."

"Then I think I'll invite him up for a week or so and see what happens," Brenna decided out loud. She wanted Tommy and Janie married as much as the rest of the family. "*I* won't do for him!"

"Good idea. Then maybe some of his caution will rub off on you."

"Do you really think I'm too impetuous?"

"Not really, honey." He gave her shoulder a squeeze. "But it will take quite a man to be able to put you in harness. I have a feeling it might turn out the other way."

"You're darn right! No man is going to control my life just because I choose to marry him!" she stated emphatically, and reached for Poco's reins, ignoring her father's laughter.

The sign announcing the Phoenix city limits heralded the end of her drive. Brenna was glad she had visited her folks. Her talk with her father had clarified a few thoughts for her, thoughts she hadn't put into words before. Marc Lawter was now a thing of the past. She couldn't live with him and still live with herself.

It would be a day-to-day existence, waiting to see when he would tire of her and who would replace her. Marc wasn't for her. It was better to be miserable alone than miserable with him. That decision made her feel better than she had felt in ages.

The phone was ringing as she entered the apartment. She dropped her bag and sweater on the floor, along with her purse, and made a nose dive for the phone.

"Hello?"

"Brenna? How did you enjoy your weekend with the folks?" It was her brother Tommy, his voice edged with humor.

"It was just what I needed, Tom," she answered breathlessly, plopping down on the couch to curl her long legs under her. "Mom told me you were down again last weekend. I'm sorry I missed seeing you."

"So am I. Mom and Dad didn't take a thing I said seriously. They enjoyed Janie though. She and Mom were forever in the kitchen doing something or other. Exchanging recipes, I guess."

"Chauvinist! They have other things to talk about besides recipes."

"Yeah!" he answered drily. "Me!"

"Oh, an egotist, too?" she teased.

"It's hard being perfect, but the rewards are great."

"When's the wedding?" Brenna changed the subject.

"I'm not sure that there will be one yet. Janie took to the family well, but would she be able to handle one of her own?"

"I've got an idea. Why don't you come up and spend some time here? It will give you and Janie time to look at things more objectively. Besides, I could use the moral support of a family member."

He fell for it. "That's a good idea. It'll give us a chance to catch up on everything. When?"

"This is Sunday. Why not come down tomorrow?" she prompted, hoping his caution would be suspended for once. If she could get him to agree, she'd hang up and leave so he couldn't call back and cancel.

"Well . . ." He hesitated.

"Oh, come on! All you need are a few clean shirts and some spare socks. What's holding you up?" she pressured, knowing it was now or never.

"All right," he agreed reluctantly. "I'll arrange

the time off and get in at about three thirty or four o'clock tomorrow afternoon.''

Brenna hung up with a smile on her face. Now let him try to weasel out of this one! She snatched her overnighter and headed for the bedroom, determined to take a shower and leave as quickly as possible. Carol was gone for two weeks visiting her own father, so the phone could ring as much as it liked. No one would be there to answer it.

As she stepped into the shower the telephone rang. She giggled, soaping herself as she hummed a tune. That had been quicker than she'd thought! Poor Thomas! How Janie had ever gotten him to the engaged stage was a miracle.

Within half an hour she was dressed in white cotton slacks, a navy blue blouse, and a blue and white seersucker jacket. Should she go to the movies or should she eat first? She applied a light coating of mascara and lipstick and snapped her purse shut with a click. She'd grab a hamburger, then select a movie. A night out, away from everyone, was just what she needed.

The doorbell pealed and Brenna jumped, startled. As far as she was aware, no one knew she had returned from her parents' home this early in the day.

As she turned the knob a strange premonition flowed through her and as she opened the door Brenna *knew* who was there. She was right.

Marc Lawter stood in the portal, his hand resting on the jamb. His eyes were alive with mischief and a darkening light that Brenna recognized as a yearning for something more intimate than talk. He never seemed to hide the fact that he wanted her and that alone was enough to frighten Brenna.

"Yes?" Her voice was curious, but distant.

"You're dining with me," he said imperiously.

"I am not!"

"Yes you are." He took her arm, beginning to pull her out the door.

Brenna twisted out of his grasp and stood facing him, her breath coming in deep gasps.

"Leave me alone, Marc Lawter. I think I've damaged my character enough by being seen with you!"

They stood glaring at each other.

The phone began to ring and she turned her head to stare at it. That would be Thomas and she couldn't answer it! They both waited uncomfortably as it rang incessantly.

"Aren't you going to answer it?"

"No," she said firmly, noting that his eyes had darkened to black. Let him think what he wanted; she didn't care.

"Either you answer it or I will—unless you spend one harmless evening in my company for dinner. What's it going to be?" He moved forward, as if he would pick up the receiver, and she placed her hand on his arm, detaining him.

"I'll go with you." She turned away to pick up her purse, knowing in her heart that she had wanted to be persuaded.

They locked the door and took the steps down to the street in silence. Marc stopped in front of a new red Ferrari. Brenna raised her eyebrows but said nothing as she slipped into the softly contoured seat. It was obviously not rented and all the small gadgets in the dashboard gave it the custom look.

"Like it?"

"Love it! Did you win a tournament?"

"Yes, lots of them, but I had this before. It was in Los Angeles, waiting for my decision on where I was going to stay."

"And you decided to stay in Phoenix?"

"I did. Surprised?" His voice was husky, making his question more personal than Brenna wanted to admit.

"Not at all. It's close to the Hollywood and Las Vegas scene. That's where your type usually hangs out, isn't it? In between tournaments, I mean."

"No. I'm usually at the golf course or in a board meeting. But nothing I say will change your mind about me. Why should I bother trying?"

He pulled up in front of an old Victorian Western restaurant on the main street of Scottsdale, a suburb of Phoenix. The quaintly historical establishment was a favorite with tourists and natives alike. The decor was straight out of a movie set, all dark wood with gold and red accessories, heavily tasseled draperies, and antique mirrors.

They were seated at a corner table and given a menu. The table was secluded, yet gave a full view of the room. The food they chose was typical Western fare: steaks, baked potatoes, salad, and beans that tasted to Brenna as if they had been cooked in an earthenware pot, simmering all day until they were tender and flavorful. The bottle of wine Marc ordered was delicious, putting Brenna in a better mood and allowing her to relax when she realized that he was asking nothing from her except to act as companion across a dinner table.

Brenna twirled her glass thoughtfully, but her eyes weren't really seeing the rich, ruby liquid as it caught the light and splintered the crystal glass into a rainbow of color. "Why did you invite me out to dinner?"

"Why not?" Marc shrugged. "I don't know many people here and I didn't want to eat alone. Besides, you're good company . . . usually."

"I see."

"I wonder if you do," he said drily, and Brenna glanced up quickly, only to see a bland expression on his face.

He was staring over her shoulder at the picture hung over the bar. It was of a woman, suggestively clothed but not nude, with golden hair and a body to rival Venus. Brenna glanced over her shoulder, then back to him.

"Beautiful, isn't she?" she asked conversationally.

"She looks hard, tough through and through. She probably eats men and spits them out whole. Most women look tender and wind up tough as nails."

"Aren't you the cynic?" Brenna questioned archly. Strange how her anger was still dormant, she thought. If anyone else had said that she would have been on her soapbox in a minute.

"Experience has made me one," he said, drinking the last of his wine.

"Some girl must have really clawed you. Just don't judge all of us by the length of our nails."

"Why not? You judge me by what you read in the newspapers. Where's the difference?" he asked softly, pouring more wine into his glass.

Brenna didn't answer; she couldn't think of anything to say. She had done just what he had accused her of. Her deep green eyes stared at his moody face and she wanted to wipe the crease from his brow, soothe the set of his chin. Suddenly she was able to see his vulnerability and it made him more human than she was ready to acknowledge.

Her heart flipped over as her mind came closer to the truth of her feelings and she deliberately tried to block them out. Her father's words returned to her; he'd said: *The only other person you really have to figure out is the guy.*

Brenna suddenly realized that, as much as she had talked to him and read about him, she really didn't know Marc. A thousand questions waited on her tongue, but she couldn't seem to get them out.

"Are you ready?" he asked, breaking into her reverie.

She blushed at being caught staring at him and nodded as she moved away from the table. The night was almost over. Let her be in control until she was home. Let her not do anything foolish.

Once more they walked in silence to the car and once more they said nothing as they drove. When they pulled up to her building she reached slowly for the door handle, but he was out of the car and had opened the door before she could do much more.

His grin was contagious. "I know a truly liberated woman wants to be able to open her own doors, but I just can't help the fact that I was brought up to believe it was my job."

She chuckled, still surrounded by the haze of the wine she'd drunk. "Among other things?"

His smile grew wicked. "Definitely. I also light cigarettes, stand up when a lady enters the room, pay the check, and expect to get invited in for coffee."

The last was the most blatant hint Brenna had ever heard and she nodded, still smiling at his easy banter. Considering the amount of wine they had consumed, a cup of coffee would do them both good. Marc hadn't stepped out of line or mentioned their last time together throughout the whole evening. Perhaps he really was lonely.

They entered the apartment and Brenna removed her jacket as she walked toward the kitchen.

"Make yourself comfortable—I won't be long."

By the time the coffee was brewing she had pulled the cups and saucers out of the cabinet. Marc had taken off his jacket and now stood in the doorway of the kitchen, lazily surveying her with predatory eyes.

For the first time since they'd reached the restaurant Brenna became nervous, wondering if she'd been wrong to invite him inside. Had she played the fool again, let down her guard and allowed him entrance into her private life when it could only lead to heartache?

Chapter Nine

"Come here," he ordered softly, holding out one arm.

Without question Brenna walked to him, needing the touch of his arms as they gently closed about her, locking her against him. It was exactly where she wanted to be. Marc sighed deeply, as if content, and her arms wrapped around his waist, her head resting on his hard chest. She could feel the power in his back and shoulder muscles as they rippled under her palms. It was heaven.

"I need you, Brenna. You're like fresh air to me," he murmured against her hair, and she cuddled closer to his lean form. She loved him and that should be enough, even if he didn't love her, too. Her wide green eyes grew wider when she realized just where her thoughts were taking her. She'd never be able to tell him of her love. That wasn't what he wanted from her. But his arms were holding her close and his soft sigh in her ear told her differently. Could he be in love with her, too?

Suddenly she remembered the female voice that had answered the phone and the lovely euphoria she was wrapped in fell aside, leaving her too vulnerable to say anything. Was he playing one off against the other? Or was it worse? Were there more than just the two of them?

"What are you thinking, Prickly Pear?" he whispered, nuzzling the small, sensitive nerve on her neck, sending chills down her back and driving all doubts away.

She couldn't put her feelings into words. They were too new for her to grasp. All she knew was that he was with her now and that meant he must feel something for her. Brenna raised her head, allowing him to see the wonder and tenderness in her eyes. Marc groaned, folding her more tightly into his arms, his lips possessively claiming hers. Brenna's whole body shivered with unbelievable excitement as she reached for his broad shoulders. She smelled the clean male scent of him and it was a heady aphrodisiac. Everything was blocked out except him. The heat from his body saturated her, leaving her weak and helpless in his arms.

Somehow they had left the doorway and were on the couch. Marc gently pushed her into the soft cushions, then hovered above her, his eyes dilated in passion. "We're so good together, darling. I touch you and suddenly I can't think straight." He unbuttoned her blouse, smoothly slipping the white pearl buttons through the small navy slits. He kissed the tip of her nose before reaching behind her back to undo her bra with a flick of his wrist. How often had he done it before? she wondered hazily, but the question had no answer. His gaze hungrily devoured what he had just uncovered, one hand lightly teasing a full, taut breast.

"I feel like I've been waiting for you all my life, Brenna. I just didn't know it until recently," he groaned thickly, allowing his weight to rest lightly on her. "Touch me, Brenna. Hold me. I can't believe I'm here and holding you in my arms again."

Brenna's clasp tightened around his neck, her back arching instinctively to his lean form. His hands were everywhere, one stroking her back, the other still claiming her breast. His thumb moved over the rosy peak to increase the heady waves coursing through her. He was a magician playing tricks on her, making her body respond with a will of its own, and now her mind was following suit. She loved him and in that knowledge lay the path she had allowed them both to walk. His tongue drew sensuous patterns on her tender flesh and she gasped, shaking with wonder as her nerves tensed into tightly coiled springs.

"I want to see you without these clothes, Brenna. I need to feel you next to me," he muttered hoarsely, pulling away.

His body was gone, leaving her cold where she had been warmed by his fire.

"Let's go. We'll go to my place, where I can lie

down and enjoy this beautiful body of yours without further interruptions." He pulled her to a sitting position before tucking his shirt into the waistband of his slacks.

Brenna watched him run a hand through his hair, oblivious to her still open blouse. Her eyes were wide, uncomprehending.

Marc smiled, tenderness and passion mixing together to touch her heart. When he held out his hands Brenna took them, holding them as she tried to steady her shaking legs.

"Marc . . ." she began hesitantly, wondering what it was she wanted to say.

"Just grab your toothbrush for tonight, sweetheart. We'll get the rest tomorrow." His dark eyes pierced hers, then he groaned, holding her close once more. "I've never let a woman get as close to me as you have and I'm sure I don't know why. All I know is that I have to have you, Brenna."

Something niggled through the fog of desire in her brain. She shook her head, stepping back in his arms and staring at him, taking in the lines of tension around his mouth and nose.

"You want me to move in with you?" she asked, praying he would say the right thing.

"Yes," he muttered, burying his lips in the softness of her hair.

"For how long?" she questioned him, her heart sinking.

"For as long as it takes for us to get each other out of our systems."

Her head almost split with the intensity of her

despair as his words soaked in. Then her despair was replaced with anger, anger that rose to such heights that it was all she could do to form words. "Get out of here, Marc! Get out and don't ever come near me again!"

He looked stunned, but Brenna was too upset to notice. A giant pain lay where her heart used to be; her breath came in short, halting gasps, as if she had been running a long distance.

His hands dropped and Brenna almost lost her balance. Her legs were shaking with reaction, but she would *never* let him know!

"Did you hear me, Marc? It's time for you to run along now and play your little games elsewhere. I'm through being your patsy."

Never had she seen anyone look so angry, but Brenna stood her ground.

"Still playing games, Brenna? The poor little virgin didn't know what she was doing and was almost seduced by the Big Bad Wolf?" he sneered. "But you're not Little Red Riding Hood and I refuse to take full blame for what *almost* happened here!" He raked her body with his eyes, controlled wrath emanating from him like an aura. "You wanted me as much as I wanted you and it's about time you faced up to yourself. You're quite something, Brenna. Are you like this with all men, or am I the only lucky one?"

"I hate you, Marc," she lied. "I'll see you burn for sweet eternity before I ever succumb to you! Now get out of here!"

His look was filled with contempt as he walked

past her toward the door. "Let me know when you outgrow your fairy tale dreams, Brenna. Though I doubt if I'll be interested anymore."

Tears gathered in her eyes and she blinked to hold them back even while she fought to hold the sobs down.

The telephone jangled and she jumped before picking it up to hold it as she would a lifeline. "Hello?" she said weakly.

Marc stood by the door, watching.

Tommy's voice came over the wire. "Brenna? Are you all right? You sound funny."

"Hi, honey! I'm fine—just seeing someone out of the apartment." And out of my life, she thought. "You're still coming, aren't you?" Her voice held a thread of hysteria.

"Well, I was going to cancel, but if you really want me to come I'll be there," he answered hesitantly, as if weighing his decision.

"Please, honey. I really do want you here. I can't wait until I see you!" she exclaimed, hoping that Marc was misinterpreting the whole conversation.

Apparently he was. By the time she placed the receiver back on the hook and turned to face him his look of anger had turned to one of utter contempt.

"Good-bye, Marc," she said slowly, somehow able to maintain her control when all she wanted was to break down and sob out her pain.

He didn't say a word, just turned and left.

The apartment was empty. Brenna crumpled to

the floor, bowing her head while the tears of loneliness and pain finally coursed freely down her cheeks.

Tommy arrived the following afternoon. He knew Brenna too well to mistake her hollow cheerful attitude for anything but what it was: despair. Finally, after two nights of pressure, he finally convinced Brenna to tell him the story.

"That creep," he growled, one fist slamming into the other. "I ought to deck him for that!"

Brenna took one look at him and began laughing, and her laughter grew louder even as her tears began to fall.

"Just what's so funny, Brenna?"

His puzzled expression only made her laugh harder and it was several minutes before she could speak. She shook her hair from her face, flipping it over her shoulders with unconscious grace. "You are! Are you so good and kind that you never made a pass at a girl just to see how far you could go? Are you going to tell me you didn't hope for the best?"

His reddened face gave her the answer even before he spoke. "That's different, Brenna. You're my sister!" he said, as if that made all the difference.

"But I'm not *his* sister, Tommy."

The sudden silence that fell was awkward and Brenna quickly changed the topic.

The next morning they packed their bathing suits, since Brenna had arranged time off from work, and headed toward Big Surf, Phoenix's answer to the coastal waters. At one end of a freshwater lagoon was a hydraulic pump that built waves up to five feet in height that splashed over four acres of soft, white sand. Swimmers and surfers alike could pretend that they were in the ocean while the pale green waves rolled on.

Brenna wore her new bikini, a beige and white striped confection that disclosed far more than it hid. She had bought it just two weeks ago on sale, but now she thought that somehow it had shrunk. It hadn't seemed half this daring in the store! She turned, shrugging. What difference did it make now? Tommy would arch a disapproving eyebrow and then she'd be in the water. Hang them all! Everyone wanted to give her directions, believing she couldn't direct herself. Her shoulders squared. Just let Tommy try to say something; she'd give him a piece of her mind!

Things worked out much as she had expected. Once Tommy got over his shock they entered the water and had a great time until, exhausted, they headed back to their towels.

Brenna reached up and pulled the pins from her hair, allowing it to fall about her shoulders in auburn abundance. Suddenly she was arrested by the sound of an all-too-familiar voice.

"Hello, Brenna. I didn't expect to see you here."

She turned to face him slowly, her eyes wide with hurt from the last time they had met. She hoped she could pull off what she was about to do.

"Hello, Marc. I thought you'd be busy on the golf course."

He stood above her, the jet waves of his hair shining in the rays of the sun.

"And I thought you'd be working." His eyes were focused on Tommy as he spoke.

"Thomas," Brenna said, "I'd like you to meet Marc Lawter. Marc, this is Thomas, from Prescott."

Tommy's eyes registered surprise before he caught on to what Brenna was doing; then he immediately got into his part. "Call me Tommy, although Tommy from Prescott sounds like the name of a song." He held out a wary hand, his smile forced. "How do you do? Brenna mentioned that she had been chauffeuring a famous golfer."

Marc ignored Tommy's outstretched hand, his face paling beneath his tan. "Will you excuse us for a moment? I'd like to talk to Brenna alone."

Brenna's eyes sparkled with anger. Taking a deep breath, she linked her arm through Tommy's. "I think we've said everything we have to say to each other. And since I have nothing to add, I don't think I need to hear your closing comments. I'll stay here—with Thomas."

The depths of Marc's eyes blazed with fury for just a moment before his expression disappeared beneath a mask of icy control. Without a word he turned and left, striding up the beach to join a beautiful blonde woman who stood waiting alone, her face a study in irritation. As soon as Marc reached her side she smiled sweetly and they walked away arm in arm.

The pain that seared through Brenna was almost

enough to make her gasp aloud and it must have shown in the whiteness of her face.

Tommy helped her to sit down, then whistled through his teeth. "So that's what Marc Lawter is like!" He shook his head in amazement. "I'm glad you're not playing around in his waters anymore, Brenna! He's a shark and you're just a poor defenseless minnow." He looked at her in puzzlement. "I can see why you were drawn to him, but he looks like he'd enjoy a more experienced woman."

"Like Cindy Chapman?" she asked bitterly.

"Was that who she was? I thought she looked familiar! But then, all beautiful women look alike to me." He tried to tease her out of her depression, knowing that there wasn't much he could do. When that failed he turned serious again. "Are you in love with him? Is that it?"

"Yes." Brenna sighed wearily, standing to fold her towel with shaky hands. "Now, if you don't mind, I'm going back to the apartment. I think I've had enough for one day."

They were back home within the hour and as Brenna washed her hair in the cool shower she tried to rid her mind of all the emotional upheaval of the afternoon. There was no use dwelling on what might have been. No matter how many times she relived the night Marc had taken her to dinner, she knew she had done the right thing. So why wasn't doing the right thing enough for her now? Her body still craved him. Her emotions still thirsted for him. Would these feelings ever go away?

Tommy knocked loudly on the door just as Brenna was drying off. "Brenna? Your illustrious godmother just called. She needs you to work tonight. She wants you there at seven thirty. And she says to make sure you don't have any uniform problems."

"All right," Brenna called through the door. Perhaps work was just what she needed.

Brenna made it to the office in plenty of time. She dressed and picked up her roster to check the call. Her face turned white. "No," she said out loud. "No!"

"No what, Brenna?" Her godmother walked into the dressing room, elegantly clad in her usual dark dress.

"Can't someone else drive Mr. Lawter?" Brenna begged with both her voice and her eyes. "I'm afraid we don't hit it off very well."

Mrs. Brussard stiffened. "No."

"But, I—" Brenna began, only to be interrupted once again.

"If you mean to object, Brenna, you can stop now. Mr. Lawter specifically asked for you. He said you knew his likes and dislikes, and since this is a special night for him I can't let him down." Her eyes grew hard. "And neither will you!"

"Yes, ma'am." Brenna sighed, wondering why she wasn't putting up as much of a fuss as she ordinarily would have. Was it because she really wanted to see Marc again? She knew it was. Who knew? He might apologize for his behavior. A little voice laughed at her assumption, but she ignored it.

Marc wanted to be picked up at an address in

Paradise Valley, a suburb of Phoenix similar to Scottsdale.

Brenna turned onto Palo Cristi Road, her mind already on what she would say and how he would respond. She quickly gave up when she realized that he wasn't likely to answer anything in the manner she thought he would. He was his own man and she had learned always to expect the unexpected from him.

If only they could make peace with each other. She shook her head, knowing there could be no peace for them when she was as committed to her view as he was to his. It didn't take much to realize that women had been falling all over him for years. Why on earth would he ever want to get married? Only she was stupid enough to imagine that he would. Only she could have chosen him to love out of all the men in the world. Only she would play the fool and *not* be in his arms, which was where she wanted to be. Well, tonight, if he so desired, that's where she would be! Brenna smiled as she thought of what his expression would be when she told him of her willingness.

The inn's lights shone against the rainbow-soft colors cast by the setting sun. She turned into the driveway and headed toward the main lodge, passing a few of the individual guest cottages along the way.

Brenna quickly glanced down at her clipboard, noting the instructions. She was to park in front and Marc would meet her on the steps at exactly seven thirty. She glanced at the small, slim gold watch on her wrist. It was seven thirty now. Where was Marc?

Brenna stepped out of the car, her eyes perusing the guests who came and went; some were dressed for the evening, others were still in tennis clothes with rackets in their hands. She could hear soft music coming from somewhere inside and remembered hearing about the excellence of the restaurant. Why would he want to eat somewhere else when this was such a delightful place? Come to think of it, why did he want her to drive him when he had his Ferrari?

A frown crossed her face, only to be erased with a smile when she saw Marc push the lobby doors open. The blood rushed through her body, then drained away to leave her face white with strain. Standing with Marc was Cindy Chapman, her body sheathed in white silk. It was an off-the-shoulder dress that smacked of a designer's touch with every wiggle of her slim hips. Her face was made up with care, pale blue eye shadow showing off her ice-blue eyes, rouge highlighting her already excellent cheekbones.

Brenna's hands clenched into fists. If he had tried, there would have been no way he could have humiliated her more. She suddenly felt bruised and hurt. Why was he doing this to her? Had she dented his precious ego? She didn't think so, but neither did she believe he was so insensitive that he didn't know how this meeting would affect her.

"Good evening." His voice was cool and impersonal, his eyes cold and indifferent. A small muscle jerked in his strong jaw, the only sign of tension.

Cindy stood next to him, watching both Marc and Brenna, obviously not recognizing their chauffeur this evening as the girl in the bikini from this afternoon. The blond actress stood impatiently by the door of the car, this time a pale gray Cadillac. Obviously she was waiting for Brenna to come out of her trance long enough to open it for her. She tapped her foot in a quick rhythm.

But Brenna didn't notice her at all. Her entire essence was concentrated solely on Marc. Her bright green eyes showed the hurt and turmoil she was going through.

Marc broke the spell with an epithet before moving quickly to open the back door before Brenna could get there and handing the svelte actress into the car.

Brenna slowly walked around to the driver's side, her mind unable to function, her feet and hands doing what was necessary without guidance. She was a robot.

She tried to ignore the couple wrapped around each other in the back seat as she slowly pulled out into traffic. Her mind was numb. Please let me get through this evening and I'll never ask another thing, she thought over and over again. Please.

Marc leaned forward. "Do you know where we're going?"

Brenna stiffened at the mockery in his voice. It was all she needed to bring her back to the present. "No, sir," she said crisply, hoping he wouldn't notice the tension in her voice.

"Take us downtown." He named one of the more popular hotel bars, then leaned back, allowing the actress to drape herself over him again. Brenna could hear the woman's voice, but not her words as she whispered into his ear. Marc's deep chuckle seemed to fill the car, infuriating Brenna even more.

So, he thought he could punish her by having her chauffeur him and his date around, did he? Well, she rather thought she could make this evening pretty unpleasant for him, too.

The curve in the road gave her a good first opportunity. She stepped on the gas and virtually skidded around the curve, throwing the actress against the door. She glanced in the mirror, only to meet Marc's angry eyes, but Brenna grinned openly as the actress picked herself up and muttered something under her breath to Marc.

"Sorry." Brenna tried hard to stifle a giggle. She almost didn't succeed, until she glanced in the mirror to see Cindy Chapman nibbling on Marc's ear. Apparently he was enjoying it, if the stupid smile on his face was anything to go by!

Brenna swerved once more, again sending Cindy to the side. Marc must have finally caught on, because he made sure the actress stayed seated next to him, but not on his lap, for the rest of the trip.

Downtown traffic was light and Brenna soon pulled up to the entrance of the plush hotel. She braked hard, throwing both passengers forward, then looked over her shoulder to apologize. "I'm sorry—this car is new to me," she said sweetly. "I'll practice while you enjoy your drinks. By the time you're ready to leave I should be better."

"You had just better improve, Brenna," Marc growled, his voice a threat.

The petulant actress jerked her head toward Brenna. "Brenna? Do you know her?" she questioned Marc sharply.

"Brenna has been my driver before, darling. But tonight she seems a little dull witted."

"My, my." The other woman's blue eyes narrowed as she took in the small, heart-shaped face under the dark gray cap and suddenly recognition dawned. "The girl at the beach!"

Brenna tipped her head. "Yes, ma'am."

"You were all wet then, too," the actress said cattily, and Marc moved with irritation, opening his door and stepping out.

Cindy Chapman hesitated. "It won't work, you know," she said softly. "You're much too obvious."

"Yes, ma'am," Brenna said wearily, suddenly very tired and a little ashamed of playing games.

"I've known Marc for a year and tonight he's asked me to marry him. If you're smart, you'll stay away." She shrugged her bare shoulder. "Because if you don't, it's your own tough luck."

She was out of the car quickly to stand with Marc, her hands grasping his arm possessively.

Marc said something to Cindy, then turned back toward the car, bending down to poke his head in the window.

"Be back here at ten o'clock sharp. We're due at a party in the canyon area."

"Then I suggest you hire a cab to take you to your car, Mr. Lawter. I'm no longer for hire."

"I already found that out. You'd make it for a short sprint, but you can't take the long race," he snapped. "But if you don't show up at ten sharp tonight, I'll make certain you're fired, Brenna!" He walked quickly into the hotel, his shoulders set in what Brenna knew was anger.

Tears finally slid down her cheeks and she swallowed hard to ease the lump in her throat. She tried to concentrate as she eased into traffic, but her tears made the stoplights look like large colored stars. She drove to the office; Marc had made up her mind for her. She had a choice of quitting or staying to take whatever torture he might want to dish out.

The decision was easy. She slipped into the parking lot, parked the car, and walked inside, hung the keys on their correct hook, signed out on the sheet left on the desk, grabbed her clothes out of her locker, and walked back out, making her way to her own small Toyota. The night air was cool on her wet cheeks, but she didn't notice.

The drive from the office to her apartment was short, so short that she didn't even realize she was home until her car stopped, seeming to have pulled into the parking lot of its own accord.

By the time she reached her apartment huge sobs wracked her body. Brenna collapsed on the couch, hiding her face in the worn cushions to muffle her cries.

Chapter Ten

Brenna must have cried for a very long time. When she finally lifted her head the apartment was in darkness. A key rattled in the door and her first thought was of Carol returning. Then she remembered that Carol was still with her father.

Tommy walked in, whistling a slightly off-key Broadway tune. He left the living room lights off as he headed for the guest bedroom, not even noticing Brenna curled up on the couch.

Brenna was relieved; she wanted to get hold of her emotions. She rose slowly and made her way to her own room, discarding the uniform she hated so much. After slipping into a pale blue shortie nightgown with a small see-through peignoir, she walked back to the kitchen. She turned on the taps and doused her face with cold water. It felt so clean against her heated skin. She berated herself for being all kinds of a fool, but it didn't stop the hurt that flooded through her body.

The doorbell rang, jangling her already tense nerves. She shuffled across the room, her shoulders slumped in despair. As she reached the door she straightened and flipped her loose hair back. Whoever it was and whatever he was selling didn't matter to her; she wasn't buying. She had already bought more than she could pay for when she had responded to the desire in Marc's eyes.

As soon as she turned the knob, the door burst open, and she fell back from the force of it, grabbing a small chair to right herself.

Marc stood in the entrance, his temper barely under control. His jet black hair looked as if he had run his fingers through it and his usually neat tie was pulled to the side. The soft fabric of his shirt heaved as he took one deep breath after another.

"What on earth do you think you're doing here?" he growled, angrily slamming the door behind him.

"I'm getting ready for bed, so if you don't mind, I won't see you out. You know the way." She turned her back to him, anger and tears mixing together in frustration.

He grabbed her shoulders, spinning her around to face him. "You little Prickly Pear! I could kill you for not waiting for me tonight." His voice was low and thick. "I went back to find you only to be told by the doorman that you had gone. When I called your office the girl on duty told me she hadn't seen you, but that you had checked out, leaving the car and keys."

"I don't sit still for threats, Marc." Brenna swallowed hard, trying to shift the lump in her throat.

His hands squeezed her shoulders, sending pain down to her fingertips, but she wouldn't tell him how much it hurt. Not for anything would she admit that!

"What's the matter, Marc? Weren't you happy with your fiancée? Why did you have to draw me into it? Haven't you humiliated me enough?" she cried, wiping her tears away quickly with the back of one hand.

"Why are you such a trial to me, Brenna?" His voice was soft, but strained. He relaxed his hands, letting them move down her arms in slow, caressing movements. His eyes traveled the length of her body, taking in the almost transparent night set. When his eyes locked with hers once more she could see the hunger in them.

"I don't mean to be, but you and I don't think the same way, Marc. I can't do what you ask of me. I thought for a while I could. But I can't!"

He pulled her close, easing her carefully into his arms as if he was afraid she would break. His hand moved under her hair, slowly stroking her neck with shaking fingers.

"I know, darling . . . I know," he murmured. "I've known the cure for our problems all along—I just didn't want to admit to it."

Her head just barely reached the curve of his neck. It fit so well there, she thought. The scent of after-shave mixed with his own distinctly male scent and she burrowed closer.

"Will you be mine, Brenna? My only woman?" he questioned softly, and she stiffened once more.

He hadn't understood a word she had said. He still wanted her to do what she couldn't.

The bedroom door opened and Tommy walked in, one hand holding a towel wrapped around his hips.

"Brenna, when did you . . . ?" He halted in mid-step, staring at the couple entwined in each other's arms.

Marc pulled away, anger and disbelief apparent in every muscle. "What are you doing here?"

"I'd like to ask you the same thing," Tommy answered angrily. "Haven't you hurt her enough?"

"Hurt her?" Marc exclaimed incredulously. Then his eyes narrowed as he took in the younger man's state of undress.

Slowly he turned back to Brenna, and what she saw in his eyes made her stomach churn. Instinctively she drew back.

"And I thought you were different. It didn't take you long to jump into bed with him, did it? Why wouldn't you do the same with me? Was it because you were trying for the gold ring? Is that it?" His voice was strained, hoarse with the depth of his emotions. His dark haunted eyes stared at her, daring her to deny what he apparently saw as the truth. "Were you afraid I wouldn't come across with a proposal if I thought you weren't pure? Is that it?" He grabbed her shoulders, shaking her.

Tommy was there before he could go on. "Leave

172

her alone and get out of here before I take you apart!" he yelled, pulling Brenna against his chest as he stared over her head at Marc.

Marc stood for a minute, then slowly turned and left the apartment. The door slammed with a resounding bang, acting as the signal for Brenna's collapse. Her body began to shake; her breathing was spasmodic as she took giant gulps of air.

Tommy, holding his towel awkwardly with one hand, led her to the couch, where she sat down, unmoving, unable to say or do anything. Marc's words kept repeating over and over in her head: *Was it because you were trying for the gold ring?*

Yes! Yes! she wanted to scream. But not for the reasons you think! I wanted to be with you always! I wanted to be with you . . . love you . . . care for you! I wanted you to want me, too! I wanted you to want me enough to make a commitment!

"Is that so wrong?"

Brenna didn't realize she'd spoken aloud until she felt Tommy's hand give hers a comforting squeeze.

"No, honey. It isn't wrong to love." He turned her toward him. "But I have to tell you, Brenna, I don't think I've ever seen a man in such pain. The agony you feel he felt, too. I keep thinking how I would feel if you were Janie and I were Marc. I think I would have killed the other man."

"Marc wouldn't. He doesn't give a hoot," she said quietly, finally calming down. "He just wanted to go to bed with me."

"I don't think so, Brenna. I think he really feels something for you."

"You're a softy. If you knew him as well as I do, you'd know his type doesn't feel deeply about anything. I'm glad he's gone!"

An early November chill was in the air. Not that it was really cold, but the mornings had a snap to them before the sun's rays warmed the air once more. The evenings, too, were cooler and Brenna was thankful for the signs of winter. Summer had been a bad season.

She picked up her small briefcase, grabbed her sweater and purse, and began running down the school hallway toward the parking lot. It was already half past four; her lesson plans had taken her longer than she had anticipated and she had promised Carol she'd do the marketing before dinner. Her small Toyota started right up, thanks to the mechanic who had charged her a small fortune last week for the new starter and tune-up. It had been paid for with money she had set aside for Robbie, who was in his first semester at college. Nothing seemed to be working out as it should. Well, almost nothing.

Brenna had the job she wanted, teaching a class full of fourth graders. Twelve weeks had passed since the final scene with Marc—twelve weeks of living in a vacuum. When school started, it had been the best thing that could have happened to Brenna. Suddenly there were new and different things to do, to get ready for, to plan. It was just the therapy she needed.

Tommy had returned to Prescott and, within the week, married Janie. The ceremony had been small and simple, but their shared happiness was immense.

Brenna smiled, driving into the parking lot of the large supermarket. One thing Tommy had learned the hard way was that absence made the heart grow less confident. Their dad had been right after all.

The supermarket was filled with people just getting off work. She pushed her cart down the aisle, ticking off a mental grocery list.

"Why, hello. Miss Gallagher, isn't it?"

Brenna spun around, curiosity turning into dread as she stared at Bette Livingston. The older woman's suit was neatly pressed, but her face looked tired. Her arms held a potpourri of ladies' toiletries.

Brenna glanced down quickly, uncomfortable under the older woman's scrutiny. "Hello, Miss Livingston. Are you living in Phoenix now?" she asked politely.

"No. I just flew in to close a deal for Marc and decided to make a mercy stop on the way to the house." She lifted her arms to show her purchases. "Every time I travel I run out of essentials, like my own brand of toothpaste or a jar of cold cream." She grinned. "Much as I try to remember my needs, I do well just to bring the contracts and closing papers."

"I see." Brenna found it hard to stand in one place when all she wanted to do was flee. A quick glance over the older woman's shoulder proved that Marc wasn't with her. Or was he?

"I hope you have a pleasant trip, Miss Livingston, but if you'll excuse me, I have to go now."

175

"Wait a minute!" Bette stopped her, her inquisitive eyes taking in Brenna's pallor. "Are you all right?" she asked.

"I'm fine."

"I just wondered if you would like two passes to the golf tournament this Saturday. It's the Arizona Open." She fished in the purse dangling from her arm and brought out two bright yellow tickets.

"I'm afraid . . ." Brenna began, almost choking on the words.

"Even if you don't use them yourself, at least give them to someone. There's no sense in wasting them," Bette interjected.

Brenna held out her hand, finally accepting the inevitable. "Thank you," she said, then quickly walked away.

Brenna called Carol's name as she entered the apartment, but there was no answer. Instead there was a note on the counter.

Brenna:

Have an important date. Don't bother making dinner for me. I'll be home late, so keep a candle in the window.

P.S. Newlyweds called. Tommy wants to talk to you about this weekend. Told him you'd return his call. Sounds like good news.

Brenna grinned as she put the groceries away, her mind consumed with the thought that Tommy had good news. Deciding not to wait for the rates to change, she walked determinedly to the telephone and dialed his number. It took forever for Janie to answer, and when she did her voice was breathless, as if she had been running.

"What are you and my brother up to, Janie?" Brenna teased. "Is he chasing you around the kitchen?"

"No, I'm lifting boxes, and now that I've got you on the phone I can't wait to tell you our good news!" She paused dramatically. "Tommy's accepted a position with a law firm in Phoenix!"

"How wonderful!"

"We'll be coming in this weekend to find a place to live," Janie continued. "Do you know any real estate agents you could recommend?"

Brenna promised to have a few names ready for them, though she silently promised herself not to recommend Lee. After exclaiming over the news once more, she hung up, humming to herself. What a wonderful surprise! She reached for her purse, remembering that one of the other teachers had given her a business card because she sold real estate as a sideline. Brenna thought that it wouldn't hurt to give her a call and see what she had to say. As she searched through her bag, the bright yellow golf passes fell out and memories of Marc came flooding back. . . .

Marc laughing . . . angry . . . loving . . . A sharp pain pierced her heart and she shoved the tickets back into her purse, burying them deep in a side pocket before suddenly retrieving them. Why not let Tommy and Janie have them? They might like something relaxing to do after a morning of house hunting. Someone ought to enjoy them. Brenna resolved to give the passes to them at the first opportunity.

The following night Carol sat across the dinner table, her mind definitely not on Brenna's meatloaf and mashed potatoes. She kept shooting sharp glances at Brenna, apparently waiting for the proper opening to discuss whatever was so important to her.

Exasperated, Brenna finally laid down her fork. "All right, Carol. What is it?"

Carol grinned sheepishly. "I just didn't want to upset you, that's all." She leaned forward, smiling nervously. "I was wondering how you would feel about finding another roommate." She looked at Brenna hesitantly. "I'm seriously considering moving back with Dad."

"Moving back? Is your dad all right?" Carol's father had lived alone since her mother had died four years ago and Brenna knew his health wasn't as good as it should be.

"Oh, no. He's fine. But I think he's lonely," Carol explained. "Besides, he could use some help with the hardware store and it's a cinch I'm not setting the world on fire here." She shrugged. "Besides, I wanted to see what the world was like and now I know. And I think I prefer to stay home until Prince Charming comes to take me away from it all," she teased.

Brenna reached over and gave Carol's hand a squeeze. "I understand and I'm happy for you. I wish you all the luck in the world. Who knows? Prince Charming might be living right next door."

"I'm hoping. As a matter of fact, there is a boy back home, but I think he's waiting for someone gorgeous to sweep him off his feet," she said wryly. "So for the last three weeks I've been on a diet. I've lost eight pounds so far and I should lose another ten in the next month." She stood to show Brenna her new figure.

"My goodness. You *have* lost weight! And to think all this has been going on right under my nose and I never noticed!"

Carol made a face and sat down once more. "Yes, but even if I turned into a stick I'd still never be as good-looking as you are or have as many men stare at me the way they do at you."

"And you don't want them to. You only need one man to love you, Carol," Brenna said sadly, not realizing how wistful she sounded. "At any rate," she went on brightly, "you look terrific and I never even noticed."

Carol's voice was serious. "You've had other things on your mind. I understand that—it's terrible to love someone and not have your love returned."

Brenna gave Carol a tight smile as she gathered their dishes together. "We've all got backpacks of sorrow, but somehow we carry our load," she quipped, hoping Carol would never know the truth of that statement.

Tommy and Janie arrived early Saturday morning. They brought with them excitement and buoyancy, which kept Brenna from retreating into the doldrums, her usual weekend mood when she wasn't occupied with plans for the children. She gave Tommy the bright yellow passes with a short explanation, ignoring her brother's searching look.

When they had gone for the day Brenna began to clean. She wore her oldest knit top and faded jeans as she set about her tasks. It was early evening by the time she finished cleaning the apartment, with only the garbage left to take out.

Damp strands of hair were sticking to the back of her neck and as she passed a mirror in the hallway she grimaced at her reflection, pulling the long tresses into an untidy pile on top of her head and securing them with a few pins. It would do until it was time to take a shower. After that she would spend the evening curled up with a new thriller and perhaps then she'd be exhausted enough to sleep through the night. Another night, another day to be lived through before school once again claimed her full attention.

All the wastebaskets were gathered together near the kitchen door, waiting for Brenna to empty them. The doorbell rang and she groaned her frustration as she poured the contents of one more wastebasket into the plastic bag. The flimsy rim folded so that half the trash landed on the floor, making her even angrier at herself.

"Come in!" Brenna shouted, her attention still on the misbehaving bag. She glanced over her shoulder and her breath left her in a rush as she stared straight into the eyes of Marc Lawter. She remained frozen in her bent position, drinking in the sight of him, suddenly realizing how hungry she had been to see his tall dark form again. A smile tugged at his lips as he took in her efforts at cleaning and the mess that had ensued.

"A treasure among trash," he said teasingly. "And a very delightful treasure, too."

Brenna stood slowly, her white face turning red as she realized his implication. Her defenses were down and for the life of her she couldn't rebuild them in time to meet his sweeping gaze. As he slowly closed the door the large apartment seemed suddenly small and claustrophobic.

She brushed a stray lock of auburn hair away from the curve of her cheek, her eyes blazing with defiance. Blast him! Why did she have to look such a mess? Why did he have to interfere in her life again? Why . . . ?

"What do you want, Marc?" Did she sound cool? She fervently hoped so. No matter what, he mustn't know that her heart was pounding loudly and her pulse beating so rapidly that the sound echoed in her ears. "I thought we had already established that you want nothing further to do with me." She was shaking from nerves; his piercing look was telling her things his words hadn't said. But she was so afraid that she was misreading that message. She stared down at the floor.

"You, Brenna, are an original, one I have to have. I think I knew it all along, but I didn't want to admit it."

"And are all your other girl friends 'originals,'

too?" She had to know, and in knowing she could lay the devil of hope, crush it forever.

"Are you talking about Cindy?" Suddenly the tension left his body and his face relaxed as he smiled down at her tenderly. At her nod he continued. "Look at me, Brenna." The words came quietly, but they were a command nonetheless. She brought her head up slowly and the love that shone from his eyes dazzled her. "I haven't even thought of Cindy since you drove into my life."

"But she stayed with you." Dejection laced her voice at his obvious lie.

"Correction. She came into town and found her way to my home."

"Isn't that one and the same?"

"No. Not when I promptly took her out to dinner, then straight to the nearest hotel, and left her there—by herself." He took a step forward. "I haven't looked at another woman since I met you, Brenna. All I can see is a fiery redhead with flashing green eyes and a perfect figure."

She couldn't say another word, nor could she move. It was as if she were rooted to the spot. She searched his face, hoping to find the cure for her tumultuous emotions.

"Why, darling? Why did you allow me to believe that you were living with another man? Why didn't you explain about your brother?" His voice showed the agony that had been eating away at him.

Her heart skipped a beat before it began again in double time. "You know?"

Marc nodded his head. "He told me after I almost

knocked him for a loop for being with another woman at the tournament. I was so mad when I saw him on the sidelines with her that I almost lost."

A dimple creased her cheek. "But you didn't."

He chuckled. "No, I didn't. I wanted to win in case they put me in jail for manslaughter and it was the last tournament I ever played." Suddenly he was sober. "But you didn't answer my question, Brenna. Why?"

Her head dropped. "Because I couldn't take the idea of your other women. I wanted to hurt you as much as you had hurt me."

"And you thought I was trying to hurt you when I came here and found you with a strange man wrapped in a towel and you wearing that tiny scrap of delectable nylon?" His eyes darkened with the memory and Brenna's heart thudded with uncontrollable excitement. "I tried so hard to forget you after that night, but the pain was unbearable. Everywhere I turned you were there, teasing me, firing my imagination. Did it hurt to see me with Cindy, Brenna? Did it hurt you as much as I hurt when I saw you with another man?" He silently begged her to answer.

"Yes," she murmured softly, her voice trembling with the confession.

He walked toward her slowly and Brenna felt her panic rise; she backed away from his arms. Once he touched her she wouldn't be able to keep her emotions under control. But he caught her, holding her against him as if he would never let her go. "When I tried to propose to you the last time we were interrupted. There's no one to interrupt us now."

"The last time . . . ?" Was she dreaming? She would never have forgotten something as important as that! Was he teasing her again? She didn't think she could stand to be played with, then forgotten.

Marc gave her a quick squeeze, smiling down with tenderness. "What do you think I was saying the night I walked in here and met your brother?"

Her expression was a mirror of the thoughts that had been tormenting her. Marc's hand wandered to her face, then moved to her chin, outlining it with caressing fingers.

"I didn't make myself very clear then, did I, darling? But I was so overwrought. To walk in and see you in that little bit of nothing was more than I was capable of handling." He sighed heavily, then stared down at her with a look that made her senses clamor for more than he was giving her. "I suddenly realized that all I wanted in the world was you. Forever."

"Even when you made me drive Cindy Chapman around, with her hanging on to you for dear life?"

He chuckled at her description. "Cindy dropped into town on her way from an engagement in Las Vegas. She surprised me and I drove her around to see the sights. I didn't know what else to do with her—except to use her to make you angry."

She drew her face away from his hand. She couldn't think straight when he was touching her like that. Her heart continued to swell with happiness, while her mind told her that this could be just

184

another story he was weaving to get whatever he was after. "But she said . . ." Brenna began, only to have Marc place his fingers gently over her mouth.

"I know. I heard her. It wasn't true, but I thought I'd let you stew in your own juices for a while. She guessed how I felt about you and reacted in her typical fashion." He hesitated for a moment, then finally decided to bare his soul. "I tried to make you jealous of Bette, too, but I couldn't. We've been friends, and nothing but friends, too long for me to use her." He groaned, pulling her closer to him, and she reveled in his capitulation, still unable to believe it was really true. "I blamed myself when I thought my behavior had driven you into another man's arms. All I wanted was you and suddenly it looked like you were gone forever."

Marc's hand stroked her waist; then he pulled her closer to him. "Stop running from what you think and face what you truly feel, my Brenna. It's not going to do you any good to hide anymore. You're mine. You always were and you always will be mine. There's no retreat from your sweet eternity."

His loving smile melted what little resistance she had left and she slipped willingly into his arms to be held tightly against his hard muscled body. Her fingers curled around his sinewy neck, holding on as if he might disappear into thin air at any minute. She could feel the dark springy hair beneath her hand and knew that she would never tire of touching him.

Once more he looked at her with his dark eyes glinting, his finger slowly tracing the outline of her mouth and jaw. As it reached her lips, she parted them, her tongue flicking the tip of his finger in a sensuous caress. The breath hissed in his throat and he bent down to taste the nectar of her mouth, searching and finding the beat of her heart with his hand over the rounded softness of her breast.

"We're getting married today."

"Impossible. How about tomorrow?" Her breath was a gasp, as was his. Her head was thrown back, giving his lips access to her slender throat as she reveled in the touch of his hands and body. No one could ever feel this wonderful—no one.

"It'll have to do." He wrapped his hand in the ringlets of her hair and gave a gentle tug, pulling the pins out and allowing it to fall about her shoulders in a mass of confusion.

"And then," he continued, "I want you in my bed, next to me, for the rest of my life." His lips tripped lightly across her skin, creating shivers of desire that consumed her. "I love you so much, Brenna," he murmured huskily. "I love you so much I'll probably spend the rest of my life boring you with the fact. I never thought I'd want to marry. That was always for others. I wanted to be free to run my life as I saw fit, not have some bossy lady tell me what to do." He pulled away, his eyes slowly blazing a path over her flushed body. "Will you be my wife?"

Her heart sang at his words. She could only nod her head before he claimed her lips once more. . . .

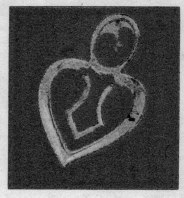

Silhouette Romance

IT'S YOUR OWN SPECIAL TIME

Contemporary romances for today's women.
Each month, six very special love stories will be yours
from SILHOUETTE. Look for them wherever books are sold
or order now from the coupon below.

$1.50 each

Hampson	☐ 1 ☐ 4 ☐ 16 ☐ 27 ☐ 28 ☐ 52 ☐ 94	Browning	☐ 12 ☐ 38 ☐ 53 ☐ 73 ☐ 93
Stanford	☐ 6 ☐ 25 ☐ 35 ☐ 46 ☐ 58 ☐ 88	Michaels	☐ 15 ☐ 32 ☐ 61 ☐ 87
		John	☐ 17 ☐ 34 ☐ 57 ☐ 85
Hastings	☐ 13 ☐ 26	Beckman	☐ 8 ☐ 37 ☐ 54 ☐ 96
Vitek	☐ 33 ☐ 47 ☐ 84	Wisdom	☐ 49 ☐ 95
Wildman	☐ 29 ☐ 48	Halston	☐ 62 ☐ 83

☐ 5 Goforth	☐ 22 Stephens	☐ 50 Scott	☐ 81 Roberts
☐ 7 Lewis	☐ 23 Edwards	☐ 55 Ladame	☐ 82 Dailey
☐ 9 Wilson	☐ 24 Healy	☐ 56 Trent	☐ 86 Adams
☐ 10 Caine	☐ 30 Dixon	☐ 59 Vernon	☐ 89 James
☐ 11 Vernon	☐ 31 Halldorson	☐ 60 Hill	☐ 90 Major
☐ 14 Oliver	☐ 36 McKay	☐ 63 Brent	☐ 92 McKay
☐ 19 Thornton	☐ 39 Sinclair	☐ 71 Ripy	☐ 97 Clay
☐ 20 Fulford	☐ 43 Robb	☐ 76 Hardy	☐ 98 St. George
☐ 21 Richards	☐ 45 Carroll	☐ 78 Oliver	☐ 99 Camp

$1.75 each

Stanford	☐ 100 ☐ 112 ☐ 131	Browning	☐ 113 ☐ 142 ☐ 164
Hardy	☐ 101 ☐ 130	Michaels	☐ 114 ☐ 146
Cork	☐ 103 ☐ 148	Beckman	☐ 124 ☐ 154
Vitek	☐ 104 ☐ 139 ☐ 157	Roberts	☐ 127 ☐ 143 ☐ 163
Dailey	☐ 106 ☐ 118 ☐ 153	Trent	☐ 110 ☐ 161
Bright	☐ 107 ☐ 125	Wisdom	☐ 132 ☐ 166
Hampson	☐ 108 ☐ 119 ☐ 128 ☐ 136 ☐ 147 ☐ 151 ☐ 155 ☐ 160	Hunter	☐ 137 ☐ 167
		Scott	☐ 117 ☐ 169

Silhouette Desire
15-Day Trial Offer
A new romance series that explores contemporary relationships in exciting detail

Six Silhouette Desire romances, free for 15 days!
We'll send you six new Silhouette Desire romances
to look over for 15 days, absolutely free! If you decide
not to keep the books, return them and owe nothing.

Six books a month, free home delivery. If you like
Silhouette Desire romances as much as we think you
will, keep them and return your payment with the
invoice. Then we will send you six new books every
month to preview, just as soon as they are published.
You pay only for the books you decide to keep, and
you never pay postage and handling.